Under
the Stairs

Under the Stairs

Alan J Hill

The Book Guild Ltd

First published in Great Britain in 2023 by
The Book Guild Ltd
Unit E2 Airfield Business Park,
Harrison Road, Market Harborough,
Leicestershire. LE16 7UL
Tel: 0116 2792299
www.bookguild.co.uk
Email: info@bookguild.co.uk
Twitter: @bookguild

Typeset in 11pt Minion Pro

Printed on FSC accredited paper
Printed and bound in Great Britain by 4edge Limited

ISBN 978 1915853 721

British Library Cataloguing in Publication Data.
A catalogue record for this book is available from the British Library.

For John James Hill
7th September 1937 to 11th October 2016

Burnley, Lancashire

1936

She hoped she was making the right decision as this would possibly affect the rest of her life. And that of her family. Elsie pondered. Away from home, she had made few friends even though she was a pretty girl; she was considered shy by her colleagues. She certainly didn't have anyone in whom she could confide. She liked James but didn't know him well. She didn't really have a lot to lose, though, as since she'd been at the manor house she had rarely ventured outside the grounds. Apart from errands. They all had to run errands.

It was 1936 and the English economy, like that of most of Europe, was in the middle of depression. Unemployment in England had risen to as high as twenty-three per cent in the early 1930s but by January 1936, when Elsie dropped into service at Gawthorpe Hall, it had fallen to a lower fourteen per cent. This was why Elsie was on her own in Burnley working as a maid and sending most of her earnings back home to St Helens. She was one of seven and if it meant moving to Burnley for employment, then so be it.

She was luckier than most; she had a job, even if she was paid half of what men were for the same work.

Gawthorpe Hall was an early seventeenth-century manor house, considered a jewel in the heart of industrial Lancashire. It was still owned and run by the Shuttleworth family, who had owned it for nearly 300 years. It was a large Elizabethan manor with seven large bedrooms, a nursery, porch and hall, drawing room and a magnificent great hall that in times past had housed many formal dinners, music performances and theatre productions. To Elsie, as she first walked up the half-mile driveway, it looked like a castle from a children's storybook.

The hall's grounds were extensive and also included a small terraced ornamental garden built in the 1850s with a view down to the river Calder at the rear of the hall. Other buildings attached to the manor house were the Great Barn, the game larder, the coach house and all the lodges and gateways situated on the two driveways to the main building. Elsie came from a two-up two-down council house in St Helens, sharing a converted parlour with her three other sisters.

At least she had a job!

Elsie was one of three maids, but the house also had a butler, housekeeper, cook and kitchen maid. Over the years, the number of servants had reduced then grown again before settling on the seven present in 1936. The deciding factor was liquid funds, and so staff numbers were equally fluid. The gardens and grounds had anything between three and seven men running around them, depending on the time of the year.

Elsie sat on a sack of potatoes in the kitchen with her back against the wall. She had finished the top-floor bedrooms and only had the second floor to clean. It was nearly eleven in the morning, and she'd decided it was time for tea and a ciggie. Cook and Dot, her help, were busying themselves preparing lunch as Elsie sneaked her unofficial break. Cook was known only as Cook and Elsie was never allowed to use the older lady's real name, just Cook. Cook admonished, "Elsie, if Mrs Dawson finds you down here, do not expect me to bail you out. You've had your warnings."

"Yes, Cook," said Elsie, who, to be fair, rarely ducked any of her chores and always got them completed to a high standard whether she took a ciggie break in the middle or not.

Dot asked, "Are you going to see him then?" Dot was fourteen, nearly fifteen years old, a local girl from Blackburn who was straight into service the day that school finished for her. This was to be her life, or so she thought, but with another war on the horizon, nobody's plans were to run true. Dot looked up to Elsie like she was a film star. Elsie was eighteen years old and had dark auburn hair that, when not hidden under a white cap, swirled around her face like a siren to the boys.

"I really don't know what to do. He's quite old, you know. I think he might be nearly thirty." Elsie said more than she normally would have in front of Cook. Mrs Dawson didn't like her girls going out on dates to the Ramsbottom 'Flicks' followed by dancing and 'Lord knows what else these young ones get up to'. Elsie was concerned that what she'd just said would get back to the housekeeper.

Earlier in the week, she'd been sent to the butcher's for some extra sausages, black puddings and a ham for Sunday. The butcher boy delivered once a week but on many an occasion, one of the younger members of the servants' quarters would have to make a trip into Burnley for extra provisions. The Shuttleworths could have ad hoc visitors who would stay over at a moment's notice, and this was one of those occasions.

As it happens, Elsie didn't mind the extra trip to the village. It was only a fifteen-minute walk to Burnley Road and as long as the weather held fair, it was a lovely walk. That particular day was a beautiful spring morning in May and so she strode out, enjoying her own company, looking every inch the young English starlet, swinging a wicker basket as she dreamt of Luise Rainer in *The Great Ziegfeld*. Elsie loved her movies or, as she called them, the films, or even 'The Flicks'.

The butcher's was next door to the Morris car showroom. *These things are cropping up everywhere*, thought Elsie, even in little Burnley. The truth was that by 1936 there were two million cars hurtling around the roads of the United Kingdom and, at the time, speed limits tended to be a suggestion rather than a law. But with car showrooms come car salesmen, and James Knowles was 'up from London' to train some young northerners in the southern dark art of 'How to sell a car'.

"All right, love. How do you fancy a spin in the back of my Morris?" and with such words, romance indeed will blossom.

Elsie had no words. She was very much a virgin in this situation. The bright lights of 'St Theresa's Catholic club under-eighteen Friday night dances' had left her with underwhelming social skills to deal with the opposite sex in the ritual of the mating game. She tried to smile which, in her nervousness and in the words of her mother, simply made her look 'a penny short of a shilling'. She managed to look even younger than her short number of years. Her smile was that of an embarrassed child caught taking a stolen biscuit from the jar.

Elsie was considered shy, but to herself she never actually felt overwhelmed or intimidated by social situations. Inside, she did not feel shy, merely lacking the social skills required. Uneducated, perhaps. There was little call in St Helens for the subtle communication of a raised eyebrow or a laugh deliberately hidden behind a gloved hand. No need for the tilted head or demure look and lowered lids that promised much more than originally suggested.

The courting ritual was far more:

"Do you come here often?"

"Can I buy you a drink?"

"Can I walk you home?"

"I fancy you; do you fancy me?"

And stage five, the one that eventually took the relationship to boyfriend/girlfriend status: "Are those Marks and Spencer's knickers?"

Not that Elsie had ever arrived at stage five; she was more a stage two girl, with the occasional innocent kiss but all within the confines of the Catholic church hall.

She tried to smile at the older man in the blue pinstripe three-piece suit, with the small stubbly moustache and Brylcreemed-smooth short back and sides but knew the smile after leaving her brain had arrived at her lips as a cross between a smirk and a grimace. She put her head back down and scuttled into the butcher's, joining the U-shaped queue around the stark white marbled floor.

Great, she thought, *that went well. He now thinks I have the intelligence of what's lying on the counter of this shop.* Unprepared but not undeterred, she promised herself that she wouldn't give up.

She wasn't a stupid girl and could hold her own in conversation with anybody, especially a car salesman. Her mum had always told her, *Hold your head up high, listen well and look anyone who speaks to you straight back in the eye. Be proud and never forget where you are from.*

She told herself this as she waited her turn to be served. Ten minutes later, she was back outside, basket fuller than when she had entered. The man was now deep in conversation with another man, similarly attired but much younger and clean-cut. They looked as though they didn't have a care in the world, but Elsie decided it was like a man talking to a boy. She chose to walk past them both rather than cross the road and avoid them. If the older man wanted to take her for a ride in his car, then why not?

As she walked past them both, she looked up at the older man, just as her mum had told her, and smiled. She always thought she could summon a twinkle to take refuge in her deep brown eyes and this was the moment. She radiated her prettiness like a warrior raising her sword. *Take that,* she thought.

James Knowles received a crucial body blow but not fatal, not even life-threatening, and parrying the warrior's sword, he stopped his conversation, excused himself with his colleague then excused himself with Elsie.

"Excuse me, young lady. My name is James Theodore Knowles."

This time better prepared, Elsie replied, "You are excused, Mr Knowles. My name is Elsie Scott."

"Pleased to meet you, Miss Scott, or may I call you Elsie?"

"No, Miss Scott will do, Mr Knowles," said Miss Scott. "For now, at least," she added, throwing a dog a bone with the promise of meat later. "How can I help you?"

James Knowles was momentarily on the back foot but quickly regained his poise.

"I was simply wondering if you would like to meet up, say, Saturday night? Perhaps the flicks or a dance? I believe Burnley has got both. What do you say?"

Elsie pondered her response. Mr Knowles was not too tall, which suited her, and was athletically built, another plus point, and his face, if a little thin, was favourable to the eye, certainly her eye. He might be a little too old and he had an accent that was far from Burnley, or Lancashire for that matter. And if he was so old, why wasn't he already taken?

Mr Knowles took her silence to be reticence or an outright 'No, thanks', a state of affairs that he was just not used to. He pushed on.

"Are you local? I've not seen you around here before. I don't normally approach girls in the street but I'm up from London and don't know many people. You smiled, I thought I'd ask. I'm selling cars, I-I-I..." Elsie kept her counsel.

Good Lord, he thought, *I'm stammering. What's this young girl doing to me?*

Miss Scott came back into the room.

"I work at Gawthorpe Hall. I've been there for about five months but I've yet to cross the doorstep to a social event outside of the servants' quarters. I think I would like to go to the cinema with you, Mr Knowles, but I'm unsure if I'll be allowed. I can't make me mind up here. Is there any way I can get in touch with you?"

James Knowles scrambled inside his jacket pocket and pulled out a raft of business cards. A real status symbol in 1936 Burnley. Trying to regain his composure, he handed one across to Elsie Scott, saying, "All the details are on the card. Morris Motors, Burnley Road. James Knowles, that's me. Burnley 485. That's the phone number. Just ask for Burnley 485. I'm here from 8am until 5pm. Monday through Friday and Saturday morning until 1pm. James, James Knowles." He paused for breath.

"Thank you, Mr Knowles. I shall be in touch." Miss Scott was enjoying herself now.

"Call me James," said James.

"Call me Miss Scott," said Miss Scott, and then laughing, added again, "I'll be in touch." She walked away a couple of strides before she looked back over her shoulder and said, "James."

James's grin split his head in two as he watched Elsie cross the street and head back to Gawthorpe.

Cook believed that Elsie was merely showing off in front of Dot. *Look at me, woman of the world being asked to the cinema by a much older man. And he wore a three-piece, obviously had a bob or two.* That's what Elsie was really saying, thought Cook. She'd only been here four and a half months and thought she owned the place.

"Right, that's enough now," said Cook. "Get yourself up off them spuds and get back to work. Same for you, Dorothy. Those veggies aren't going to peel themselves." Elsie did as she was told and scrambled to her feet, wiping her maid's uniform down from the dry soil that had dirtied her from the potato sack.

"Sorry, Cook. Just excited, is all. I'll work harder this afternoon to make up for my fag break." Elsie decided it was time to be contrite rather than cocky. She left the warmth of the kitchen and was away to clean the last three bedrooms, although two of them only needed dusting as she couldn't remember them being used since she'd been at Gawthorpe. Up the narrow back stairs, into the main hall and then up the main double staircase that thrust from the ground floor almost directly from the porch to the sweep of the first-floor balcony. Around the balcony and then up one of the smaller side staircases to the second floor and the final three bedrooms.

While the depression had diminished in most of the country, it was still prevalent in the north of England and over twenty per cent of young women were sent out to service. The biggest employer of women after service was working as shop assistants, with eight per cent of all young girls, but only four out of every ten managed to find employment of any kind. So, when Elsie thought she was lucky to have a job, she was right, and she didn't want to lose it.

Imagine the shame of having to return home when she was the only girl in her family to hold down any work. Her three brothers had all managed to find occupation. Industry in St Helens was strong and two worked down one of the several coal pits that surrounded the town like jackals bringing down its prey. Her younger brother had managed to get himself a manufacturing role making Beecham's Pills at the factory near the town centre. Job for life, they'd said. He would die in France in 1940, but that story is still in Elsie's future.

She cleaned, scrubbed and worked hard, not just today but every day. She would skive the odd ciggie break or nip to the kitchen for a cup of tea, but no one could ever complain about either her industry or the quality of her work. As her mum told her, *Never forget where you're from.* That day, the time flew, because as with all favourable memories, the mind starts to dress them up in their Sunday best so that James Knowles adopted movie star looks in her recollection. Plus, she believed she held the upper hand. He liked her; she knew it. Or as her coarse sister Carol might say, *He fancies the pants off you.*

The next task was to accept his invitation, but how was she to do that? If she asked for use of the Shuttleworths' phone, the questions would start raining down on her like hailstones in a storm. She didn't actually know anybody with a phone and if she needed to contact home, had to write a letter. In an emergency, she could ring St Theresa's Church, and Father Doyle would get a message to her mum or dad. She mused, *How am I going to let him know that I want to go?* Why didn't she just say yes there and then? Why did she have to 'play the game'? A game that she didn't know the rules for and one in which the rules were rewritten every other week anyway.

Today was Thursday; she had until Saturday morning to figure something out. Either she had to chance her arm and 'borrow' the phone that sat on the small living-room table by the fireside, or she had to get back into town again. Then, once she accepted, she had to get Mrs Dawson to agree to her having Saturday night off. How could she possibly arrange all this? Help came from an unexpected direction.

As they were all taking their dinner that night in the servants' quarters, Elsie was no closer to finding a solution. The outdoor lads were all huddled together at one end of the table giggling and whispering. Occasionally, a voice would be raised, but as far as Elsie was concerned, they spoke a different language out in the grounds. French, German or even a made-up language like Elvish or something. She hardly understood a word they said.

Mrs Dawson was talking to Mr Dawson, the head butler, same name but no relation, everyone said, but Elsie had her doubts. They both had the same little eyes and pointed noses and in silhouette looked like Mr and Mrs Punch, straight from Southport beach. Mr Dawson was talking about a phone call that her ladyship had taken earlier that evening and Elsie Scott saw it as her opportunity. One that she would have to take if she was ever going to get to the cinema on Saturday night.

"I've never made a phone call," she chirped, pretending to take little notice generally of the conversation. "If there's an emergency, I wouldn't have an idea what to do."

Mr Dawson cleared his throat as if he was about to announce the abdication of the king.

"Don't be silly, girl. If there was an emergency, we wouldn't be relying on you to make a call."

"But what about when I'm acting maid-in-waiting for her ladyship. What if she took one of her turns and was half dressed? I couldn't have just anyone running in. Her ladyship would be liable to take another funny turn if Mr Dawson came to her rescue and she was in a state of undress, I'm sure. None of the others know how to make a call either."

There was a shaking of heads around the table. Even Cook and Mrs Dawson answered in the negative with a whip of their heads, which for all the world looked like a couple of horses shaking their manes in the paddock. Elsie continued.

"Well, I'd even go as far as to say that Mr Dawson couldn't make a phone call."

"You silly girl, of course I can make a phone call," harumphed the head butler, in obvious annoyance.

"Well, fine, I thought you could," ploughed on Elsie, contradicting herself but in full flow now. "But what if you was away with his lordship, on a shoot, or his club, or wherever else you go to on his trips."

Full-blown sniggers from around the table this time, especially from the groundsmen or lads.

"Her ladyship would be mortified when she asked me to make a call and I didn't know how. Especially when I told her I knew this would happen, but nobody taught me."

Elsie chose this moment to slurp another spoonful of her vegetable soup and mop some up with her bread. As if to say, *There you go, said my piece, I'm safe having my dinner. Let the grown-ups deal with the problem.*

Mr Dawson said, "Join me upstairs after your meal. I'll show you how the phone works, just in case of emergencies."

Oh, I see, thought Elsie, *it was all your idea in the first place,* but she wasn't worried. She had worked her opportunity. Her next task was to get Mrs Dawson to agree to her trip to town on Saturday night. She wasn't working Saturday night; none of them were. The Shuttleworths were off on a trip somewhere. Yet, another May ball (*I thought we were still coming out of depression or something*, thought Elsie), but it meant she had no duties.

She had high hopes that she would be meeting up with Mr James Knowles after all. She wasn't particularly good with numbers, but 'Burnley 485' was etched on her brain like symbols scraped in ice on a frosty window. She knew that if she didn't use the numbers quickly, the thaw would erase them forever.

Elsie said little else at the table. She had now created her opportunity; she just had to take it. *The course of true love shouldn't be this difficult*, she thought. Then realised what she was inferring: *'True Love'. I've only said three sentences to the man*. Nevertheless, meeting Mr Knowles had taken on an importance to her that was completely out of proportion with the date itself, as that was what it was, a date. If she accepted and then managed to get to Burnley.

Finishing her soup and bread, she waited for Mr Dawson to give her the nod, which is exactly what he did. He scraped his bowl clean, then lit and smoked his pipe for fifteen minutes (*He's doing that on purpose to keep me waiting*, thought Elsie), before literally nodding at her to follow him upstairs. He self-importantly marched her to the phone in the drawing room. The phone was as big and black as a large cat sat imperiously on the table next to the 6-foot-wide hearth and fireplace, just bearing cinders at this time of the year.

"Firstly, you pick the phone up like this, holding the end without the cord attached to your ear, as so, and the other end to your mouth. As so."

"I said I'd never used one, Mr Dawson, not that I'd never seen one used. I know which end to talk into," laughed Elsie. Mr Dawson did not laugh back.

"Cheek, girl. Not so much of it, please. Secondly, you rattle the receiver until you get the Burnley exchange, as such." Dawson waited before speaking. "Mrs Shacklady, good evening. No, I don't need a number. I'm merely teaching one of the maids how to use the phone in case of an emergency. No, I don't need the emergency services. No police. No fire service. No ambulance. I didn't ask for the emergency services. No, I didn't say I had an emergency. Good night to you as well, Mrs Shacklady."

"Well, that went well," said Elsie, ignoring the previous comment about less cheek.

"Get back down those stairs. NOW." He didn't often raise his voice but now seemed a suitable time to do so, evidently chastised, but instead of trotting down the servants' back stairwell, she double backed into the shadow beneath the main staircase. Under the stairs, she crouched down and watched as several minutes later Mr Dawson strutted past, muttering incoherently under his breath. This was the chance she had been trying to manufacture. She went straight back to the phone and, following her instructions perfectly, soon had Mrs Shacklady back on the other end.

"Burnley 485, please. Yes, I'll wait."

Moments later, "'Ello."

"Is that the Morris garage on Burnley Road?"

"Aye."

"May I speak to Mr Knowles, please?"

"He buggered off 'ours ago. This is Fred, can I 'elp?"

"Please can you give him a message? Would you tell him that Miss Scott will meet him at 7pm outside the Burnley Empire on Saturday night?"

"Aye," and with that Fred put the phone down. Fred was known in Burnley village for not using one word when none would suffice. Elsie had done all she could and, replacing the receiver, hurried back to the kitchen before she was missed.

"Where have you been?" asked Mr and Mrs Dawson (no relation) in unison.

"Women's troubles," shot back Elsie, which, as her mum had told her correctly, would stop any conversation dead in its tracks!

Hampton, London

1977

The Churches had lived in Old Road for over eighty years and during their time, there had been changes. For a start, they now had a carpeted living room when once there had only been linoleum, or lino. Oh, and in approximately the same time span, JFK had fulfilled his mission statement and 'put a man on the moon by the end of the decade', the '60s; only he wasn't there to see it. Mary Johnson had married Norbert Church on his week's leave from the navy in 1957 and they had lived in Old Road ever since. But Bert's dad, as Norbert was known, and his grandad before him, had lived in the same house.

A two-up two-down Edwardian semi-detached, with an extension to build a kitchen and inside bathroom. The gap between the semi-detached houses was approximately four inches and from the front of the road the array of houses looked like a string of terraced abodes. As long as they had lived there, blessed with an only daughter called Jayne in

1960, Uncle Ted had lived next door. Before Uncle Ted, his extended family had lived in the house until eventually he had managed to buy it for himself.

Uncle Ted was a World War II veteran and a World War II widower, whose only child had moved away to America not long after his wife died. He wouldn't go. London, even the leafy suburbs like Hampton, was his 'manor' and he wasn't going anywhere. His decision left him both lonely and alone, not always the same state of affairs. He relied upon the generosity and goodwill of his neighbours and friends to help him out.

He never went anywhere without two vital items. One was the lump of shrapnel that had lodged in his burned shoulder in North Africa in 1943, which had also given him chronic lung problems. The second was the constant mental health issues that he'd brought back with him from Rommel's desert attacks. The issues that woke him at night, over thirty years later, sweating and screaming, believing his bed was on fire. He knew how fortunate he'd been through life just getting to his seventies, but at this late stage, with the threat of death a constant companion, he knew how lucky he was to have two such good souls as Mary and Bert as his immediate neighbours.

Without putting too fine a point on it, they had been his Guardian Angels as he'd slowly lost mobility through his physical injuries, but neither knew what mental anguish he put himself through. How could he tell Bert that he sometimes woke from sleep crying and screaming? That was something he quite simply couldn't bring himself to admit. Alone and lonely, with his own thoughts and fears and no sounding board to offload his anxieties.

Uncle Ted – uncle to whom nobody knew – never let his illnesses define him. He tried to be a good neighbour and was forever leaning over the picket fence at the rear of the house separating him from number 41, where Mary and Bert lived. He did like a good natter and his neighbours were only too glad to natter back. His pride and joy was his back garden, in which he spent the majority of his waking hours. The gardens in Old Road were a real feature of these vintage houses as they extended for over 120 feet in a straight line from the back of the house, really unusual for this part of an overcrowded London suburb.

The gardens were relatively narrow, being the exact width of the houses themselves, but then extended away, more than twice the length of a contemporary London garden. Ted's garden was a mix of a small lawn, large hardy bushes, full borders of bedding plants and then a vegetable garden at the furthermost point complemented by a homemade greenhouse.

All along the perimeter of the garden masking the fences, both the large one on the outside and the picket one between the houses, he had a selection of what he called his hedging plants. Red Berberis was his favourite, which complemented the Mexican Orange Blossom, Silver Holly and the reds of the Red Robins and Firethorn, and finally all gaps were plugged with a variety of lavenders, which meant there was always a fug of vibrant scents in the air.

Part of the plot was his 'English garden' in which he grew many flowers that may have originated in other countries but were ones that Ted considered to be quintessentially 'English'. Delphiniums cast their shadows over tall Foxgloves that sat next to Chrysanthemums, Geraniums and Dahlias. He had a joke with Bert that he only ever grew bedding plants that ended in the letter A, so his annuals planted in spring were Begonias, Fuchsias, Petunias and Gazanias. Finally, his rose garden used to win awards; there were so many varieties and colours.

His vegetable patch was less exotic, with the standard potatoes, carrots, turnips and swedes. In his see-through plastic hand-crafted greenhouse, he covered the staples of tomatoes and cucumbers. Whatever his life had been prior to going to the war, his life post the war revolved around his love of being outdoors and cultivating his garden. Many of his products made their way over the picket fence and into the pots and pans on Mary's stove, for which in return he would get a good dinner coupled with some company and a glass of wine.

Then in the summer of 1977, he started to feel ill. It seemed he may have brought a third gift back with him from South Africa in 1943. Every branch of the armed forces used asbestos in the construction of ships, tanks, trucks, aircraft, barracks and other buildings. The military purchased asbestos products from manufacturers who allegedly withheld information about the dangers of inhaling the toxic mineral. Be that as it may, proven or unproven, Ted had spent so much time in tanks and barracks that he had been holding fibres in his lungs for twenty or more years and had asbestosis. In 1977, this had turned into lung cancer. No doctor could tell Ted for sure that it was as a result of his time spent fighting for the freedom of our country in World War II.

He sat across the kitchen table in Mary and Bert's extension to the four original rooms.

"I've something to tell you both," he said. Both Mary and Bert knew what was coming. They weren't stupid people and had been discussing for a while Ted's unquestionable decline. He was never a tall man, a stocky 5 foot 7 or 8, but as the years wore him down his posture was increasingly stooped, coupled with his incessant coughing and spluttering that had started several years earlier but had never gone away. They both feared the worst. Ted delivered the worst.

"Doctors have told me my lungs are done for, cancer." As he made his pronouncement, he lit up a cigarette. "They're going to give me something called chemo, something or other. Chemicals that help break down the cancer cells. But they have warned me that it doesn't work for everyone. But they did say that I might last another five years."

Mary dabbed at her eyes with her handkerchief, not being one for getting overemotional. Bert took the positive outlook.

"Well, that's good news and bad news, isn't it. Lung cancer can take you quicker than that normally, so at least you've got a go at it."

"Chemotherapy," said Mary. "That's what it's called. They give you injections for a few weeks. Makes you quite ill apparently."

"I couldn't be any bloody worse, could I?" laughed Ted.

"When does it start?" asked Bert.

"Week on Tuesday. Just in time to miss the queen's jubilee. I'm not much of a fan of street parties. Anyway, it's a warm one today so I need to water the garden, so I'll see you later." And with that he was gone, not one for standing on ceremony; he had delivered his 'news' and that was it. Ted went out the back way and even in his seventies could bunk himself over the fence back onto his own property.

Bert and Mary finished their tea and put the cups in the sink.

St Helens, Merseyside

1975

It was the year that inflation hit over twenty-four per cent and the price of petrol went up more than seventy per cent in one year, but I wasn't bothered. We think we've got it bad now in 2022 as inflation hits ten per cent. Did you live through the '70s? I did. Harold Wilson was prime minister, but the Conservatives had just elected their first-ever female leader. The name's Thatcher, Margaret Thatcher. Which reminds me that Roger Moore was James Bond and had just started with the double whammy of *Live and Let Die* and *The Man with the Golden Gun*. Me and my mates cheered when that car did the full 360 degrees spin, and in 1975, in England, in the cinema, no one ever cheered.

But I wasn't bothered. Me and my mates queued around the block three times before we got in to see *Jaws* and it was on at the Savoy for twenty-one weeks, or at least that was what we all told each other. But it was definitely on for all summer that year. I think by the end we'd seen it at least five times each and we all still jumped out of our seats when the head fell out the bottom of the boat. If you wanted to see a new movie more than once in 1975, you had to go back to the cinema. It took at least three years for a new release to get on one of the three – yes, just three – TV channels available. And the battle between VHS and Betamax was about to begin. But I wasn't bothered.

The music was all over the place in 1975. The Stylistics had the biggest hit of the summer with *Can't Give You Anything (But My Love)*. Rod Stewart was *Sailing* everywhere, Jasper Carrott was riding his *Funky Moped*, the Bee Gees were *Jive Talkin'*, and a bloke called Bowie had his first USA number one single with *Fame*, but I wasn't bothered. (He only ever had one more, *Let's Dance* in 1983, and it took his death before he had a number one album, *Blackstar*. Not sure the Americans got him like we did.)

I wasn't bothered because 1975 was the hottest summer since 1947, and I had turned fourteen in June and been allowed to stay home alone for the summer holidays during the day while my mum and dad worked. My younger sister and brother had to be minded by my nan in Farnworth Street, Fingerpost as they were only twelve and ten. And I wasn't BOTHERED! Why should I be as I had six weeks of freedom to do as I wanted?

Dad used to work as an employment officer in those days; he was kept busy in St Helens in 1975 and used to come home for lunch to check up on me. My job was to have some soup on the go and butter some bread and if he were flush, he'd buy us each a Pimbletts pie, still unofficially the best pies on the planet, to fill us up. Either steak – misnomer – or meat and potato. It was the best meal in the world.

There were seven of us in our gang. Now when I say gang, please do not get connotations of us running around inner cities as mules and handlers for the crack cocaine dealers. This was St Helens in the '70s and drugs was something they made at the Beecham's Factory on Westfield Street in the form of powders and pills. So, when I say gang, I mean friends who you played football and rugby with during winter and cricket in summer, you went on walks with around Carr Mill Dam and went on adventures with in the woods, either on foot or on bikes. We knew them as 'The Woods'. It's now known as Redpool Estate (just over two acres), but we never called it that back then.

Our unofficial and never legally elected leader was an older lad who I'd grown up with from around the corner called Charlie. He was leader because he was eldest, clever and quite good at sport. What more do you look for in a leader? His unofficial and never legally elected vice-leader was Faz. He was also joint eldest, cleverer than Charlie but not quite as good at sports and therefore not seen out with the gang as much. A steady number two should Charlie not turn up.

The pecking order for the rest of us depended on a whole catalogue of criteria, inter-dependencies and parameters. With no weighting and in no particular order, fighting skills, bravado, common sense, intelligence, humour and ability to make everyone else laugh, sporting prowess, which obviously varied depending on the sport, size of bike (more on this later), bottle, cheekiness, whether you had a car and your mum or dad would give lifts, parents' attitude to access to our houses (if on a rainy night your mum allowed your mates in to play board games, you was king for the day) and finally how much money you had in your pocket, which for most of us was, as we say up north, 'nowt'.

So, back to the members which I'm relaying in age as that's how I remember us. Lee and Chris, the Dobey twins, were next. They were somewhere in age between the three youngest, that included me, and the two eldest, Charlie and Faz. They were the newest members of the gang as they had moved to Redpool as fully formed children from somewhere in Liverpool, whereas the rest of us were born-and-bred locals. Lee was known as Lee, some people just don't get nicknames, but his brother Chris had an unfortunate twitch in which he seemed to blink his eyes three times more per second than the next lad and so got the unfortunate name cast on him at school of 'Kodak'. Kids can be so cruel.

Due to the fact that at different points of our education we all spent time at the same school, the name Kodak came home with Chris as well as being regularly used as his school nickname. He hated it and we only used it when there was some argument going on with him involved. He had a fiery temper and was a big lad who could handle himself, so I think at one time or another the four other junior members of the gang took a right hiding off him, including his twin, which we all probably deserved.

Then there was Mush, Charlie's younger brother, whose real name was Luke but as Charlie fed him on bullshit, Mushroom became Mush. Number six was Faz's younger brother, who was by far the smallest of the seven of us and had a tiny little bike that he had to pedal three times as fast as the rest just to keep up. He was known as Inchy after a kid's

25

American cartoon series that only ran for thirteen episodes in 1973 called *Inch Eye, Private Eye*, about a tiny little detective in the States. Then there was me, Graham Holmes, known as Locky. Sherlock reduced to Lock and then, as with most nicknames, someone added a Y. And I wasn't bothered.

In chronological order, if that's the right word, our gang was Charlie, Faz, Lee, Kodak, Mush, Locky and Inchy, and sometime in July or August we set off on a bike ride that we'd never forget and, trust me, I would be very bothered.

It was a beautiful summer's morning not long after 9.30am and we had decided to go to the far end of the woods, near the East Lancs road, where someone had built a fantastic rope swing over a babbling stream. This part of the woods had three tiers, with a path on the bottom to the left side of the brook. On the right of it, the swing side, there was a steep hill with a second path at the top which at this section of the forest ran in parallel to the path and brook at the bottom. The third level, another steep hill, continued to the right of the second path up into no man's land, actually farmer's land that remained unexplored. Both the two paths meandered their ways at the bottom and top of the lowest tier, through the trees and cut their own different bike tracks.

Two thirds of the way up the first slope was a humungous oak tree that had grown up and out and left and right, with branches sticking out everywhere. It was shaped more like a very large bush than a tree, but one of the branches jutted out on its own over the slope like a signpost pointing us all back home. This was where the rope had been attached so you could climb onto the branch, which had been tied onto the bottom of the rope as a seat. The terrace wasn't very wide here and the slope started again behind you for another twenty yards or more. So, from the bottom to the top: path, stream, slope, tree, swing, launching point, path, slope!

We had hurtled along the top path to arrive at the launching point of the swing, and when I say hurtled, I mean like seven carriages of an express runaway train careering towards the ravine with the heroine tied to the front. We had no regard for our own safety or that of others, but at that age you are indestructible. We never had a major incident but someone would occasionally come off or end up thrown off the path into a patch of stinging nettles. The path was narrow, and winding left and right with many blind corners, but that didn't seem to bother us.

The pecking order was Charlie at the front followed by Faz, then the twins. I managed to finagle myself into fifth place somehow even though Mush was older than me and had a slightly bigger bike. Bringing up the rear, legs spiralling so fast that if they touched, he'd start a forest fire, came Inchy. I had recently discovered swearing as an art form and tried to get a swear word into every sentence.

The sentence, *Look at that strange-looking tree over there*, would probably have come out, "Oi, knobheads. That fucking tree looks like a big dick!" I know I said art form, but it wasn't high art. The point being that my liberal use of lesser-known parts of the Queen's English nabbed me the fifth spot on the cycling hierarchical ladder. Swearing amongst a gang of lads was very important, and if you could make it funny as well, lots of kudos.

We arrived at the swing all sweaty, so our first task was to strip to the waist. Not all of us. Charlie and Faz were too old now for that kind of behaviour. So were 'The Twins' to be honest, but they were just big daft lads. We then proceeded to run down the hill and splash around in the chilly water for a while until we were wet rather than dry. Didn't matter, who cared; we'd be dry again in five minutes. We did have to stay upstream of a dead squirrel, though, which Kodak was poking with a stick.

"Maggots are coming out," he shouted, and we all ran over for a look. Kodak then proceeded to chase us all with the squirrel end of the stick he'd been poking it with.

A communal aargh was heard around the woods as we scattered in all directions, with me shouting something encouraging like, "Piss off, you tosser."

Charlie and Faz were watching this drama unfurl from the safety of the top of the hill. The backdrop to them was a slope full of bluebells, although most had died away, sticking up from thick grass as the second hill reached backwards to the hazy blue sky. To this day, I remember thinking they glowed like creatures from another planet, like in one of the science fiction books I always had my nose buried in at that age. We never climbed the hill behind them, don't know why. The bikes wouldn't easily go up and there was a farmer's field at the top, but we never left the top path.

Charlie took control.

"Kids, do you want a go on the swing or not? I'm going if you don't get up here." It was Charlie's regular threat that always worked as he was by far the most measured, sensible and collected of us all, and we couldn't imagine going on a day out without his calm presence. I think I also knew that this would probably be the last summer we all spent together like this, as Charlie and Faz were outgrowing the rest of us.

Kodak dropped the squirrel maggot-infected stick and we all climbed back up to the launch pad. I knew Charlie was a good leader because he didn't insist that he went first unless someone challenged him on it or tried to push ahead of him, then he would exert his authority, but I never remember him ever having to raise his fist at any one of us. The rest of us had always scrapped with each other at one turn or another; nothing serious that we couldn't patch up later.

For the rest of this hot, sweaty morning, we took turns swinging out over the brook. The water was not deep enough to drop into, but we did run down the hill, with our tops discarded, and splashed about in the cold brook water to keep cool. Upstream from the squirrel, of course. We had been doing this for about an hour when it happened. The twins were in the water; Mush was on the swing. The rest of us sat waiting for our turn; Charlie was pushing his brother. I was facing down the slope towards the stream, but I honestly felt the air around us change. The lads at the midpoint of the hill stopped talking. Mush, on the swing, stopped screaming his pleasure. Kodak and Lee splashed on for a while before they too stopped in their tracks.

Mush was now swinging lazily back and forth, slowing down as no one was pushing him. I sat up and turned as everyone was staring open-mouthed back up the hill behind us, towards the farmer's field. We all grew up that day, as there at the top of the hill was a man. Far enough away to not approach us quickly but clear as day in the dreamy light that filtered around him. If he hadn't had his erect penis in his hand, which he was waving in our general direction, you might even have said the scene was ethereal.

I shouted, "DICK", but then someone else shouted something far more useful:

"BIKES," and we didn't need a second invitation. Apart from Mush, who had now stopped swinging and was perched a good 10 foot plus above the brook. We were all on our bikes, formation forgotten, and were scrambling in the opposite direction from 'Dick Man'. Charlie stopped, jumped off his bike, ran back for his brother and helped him down before we were all on our way again. (Charlie became a bit of a folk hero for this act of bravery.) We never regrouped that day. We all went to our own homes, apart from me; I went back to Charlie and Mush's, they were my besties.

We told Charlie's mum, Jean, all about it and then I got a fit of the giggles, and when I say giggles… I became hysterical. You know what that kind of laughter is like; it's more contagious than COVID and in a moment we were howling like the three hyenas from *The Lion King*. The more we tried to tell the tale, the funnier it got to us, until the three of us were lying on the floor with tears running down our cheeks. I can hand on heart say that I'd never laughed that way before, and I haven't since.

Charlie and Mush's mum sent me home. She had worked out the gist of the story and had decided we needed to be separated for a while to calm down. Over the next week, we all met up again and eventually went to the swing in the woods once more but never saw the man again, who we called Richard; think about it. It was an adventure we spoke about for years, but I believe for most of us it was the day that the twilight of childhood crept into the dusk of adulthood. Life was an adventure but had real grown-up dangers, and some of them hid in the woods and waited for you to come out and play!

The real point of this story, though, is that when I got home, I soon became bored and went rooting under the stairs to find my football boots for a kickaround on my own on the back field. I'll never forget this day my entire life because if the morning was a coming-of-age experience for me, what I found under the stairs introduced me to adulthood before I was prepared to go there.

Preston, Suez and the Mediterranean Sea

1959

The *Empire Fowey* – 1959

The ship was a German build captured in 1945 as the *SS Potsdam* and renamed as the *Empire Jewel*, but it was rebuilt in 1947 as the *Empire Fowey*, named after the river in Cornwall. The rebuild had cost the best part of £3 million but afterwards was able to carry 1,636 troops. In 1959, one of these was Private 23627023 James Holmes, most recently of Harris Avenue, St Helens.

James Holmes had originally wanted to join the RAF at the age of fifteen, but his older brother Frank had put a stop to that.

"We need the money," he'd been told. "You'll have to cut glass at Pilks like the rest of us." Jimmy, as James always felt 'too proper', had had to wait for his National Service call-up at the age of twenty-one, but as it happened, he had to wait another nine months because of 'cutbacks'. If he hadn't been learning the trade of glass cutter at Pilkington Brothers, he would have been called at eighteen, not twenty-one. Suez and Berlin made sure that the cutbacks were not permanent and so in June 1959, Jimmy got his papers and joined the Lancashire Regiment. This soon became the Lancaster Regiment, to cover a greater width and geographical area of the north-west of England. It was something he had always wanted to do.

His first ten weeks of service were spent in Fulwood Barracks, Preston, where he did his basic infantryman training. After his obligatory medical, 'Cough', Jimmy had to then get used to military life. Men thrown together from all different demographics of the region just had to get on with it, but Jimmy was a cocky young man, the youngest of six kids, two who had died very young. He was used to fighting for everything, even a seat at the table for dinner as there weren't enough chairs to go around. Frank, the eldest, then May, Kenneth and then Jimmy. His parents had also died young, just as Jimmy had reached double figures, and he was thankful to May for bringing him and his brothers up.

He hadn't got to know his parents well but loved his brothers deeply, and May even more so for replacing the absent mother, Marie, and his brothers more than made up for the missing David Holmes, his father. May always had a smile on her face no matter what scrapes the three brothers got themselves into, and Jimmy, as the youngest, was always the scapegoat. He once came home black and blue with bruises and wet through after Ken and Frank had found (May suspected it was never lost) an old tractor tyre. Jimmy was the one who had to curl himself into it and get pushed down the hill that was Alder Hey Road.

The tyre had bounced down the hill, hit the kerb, flown over the hedge and landed in the brook. Jimmy was soaked to the skin, covered in nettle stings and eventually started to turn purple with the bruising. This was the picture that formed the cheeky character that Jimmy took into the barracks with him in 1959, plus he was one of the few twenty-one-year-olds versus the majority of the eighteen-year-old recruits.

Once enlisted and having been in their new home for ten weeks, the servicemen were issued with their equipment, which consisted of, but not exclusively, uniforms fitted or otherwise; two pairs of boots and one pair of army plimsolls; four cleaning brushes; several towels, flannels, soaps and cleaning materials; two tin food containers; and numerous other bits and pieces that when laid out on their bed or cot filled it from one end to the other.

Private G***** K*****, Royal Army Medical Corps – "My battle dress blouse fitted me perfectly so the quartermaster sergeant apologised and assured me it didn't usually happen."

Jimmy and his newfound friends, 'Ginger' Fay from the Moss Side of Manchester and little Jock from somewhere in the Lake District, who once went up to Edinburgh for New Year, hence 'Jock', began what became the seemingly endless polishing of kit and equipment. Ginger was unsurprisingly a flame-haired young man and built like a Moss Side warehouse. Jimmy became known as Rocky.

Ginger said Jimmy was paler than he was and looked like he'd come from under a rock. The nickname became quite the antithesis of its meaning as Jimmy eventually became a dark-skinned brown colour under the far eastern climate.

Training was severe. The sergeants were under pressure to train the new conscripts in as short a time as possible. Some crumbled but Jimmy loved it. Was this mindless drill aimed at destroying individualism or engendering a group identity and bringing the new infantrymen closer as a unit?

The living conditions in the barracks were either too cold or too hot. It was June, becoming July, so was too hot for the newly christened Rocky and his mates but as Rocky said, "It was always too hot at home in summer so nothing new here."

Ginger replied, "Fuck off, Rocky. I'm loving this. I haven't been warm on Moss Side since 1941, and that's only because the Jerries bombed us and set the place on fire. Give me the warm any day."

"It's not the heat, man. It's the stinking bogs and trying to get your uniform clean. They are my problems," said Jock.

"You big tart," said Ginger. "The Lake District has made you soft." Jock and Rocky didn't argue, even though Ginger was a good mate. Or at this stage potentially a good mate; he looked like he could rip your head off and not think twice about it. They both decided to stay on the right side of him and keep their own counsel for now. Or at least until they knew him better.

The barracks didn't just house these three but another seventeen men, ten barrack beds lining either side of the room just like the soldiers themselves out on parade. At one end of the barracks was the washroom. Eight sinks and about the same number of showers, which emitted a lukewarm spray of rust-coloured water. Each man had a steel wardrobe, an iron bed and one footlocker for smaller items of kit and personal effects such as photos of loved ones.

Lance Corporal A**** C***** of the Royal Engineers – "Endless drilling, gruelling inspections, physical training, rifle practice, polishing boots and equipment, cross-country runs, lectures in the art of warfare, fatigues of all sorts and all the time corporals and sergeants continually shouting and swearing from morning till night."

After six weeks of intensive training, cleaning, drilling and the dreaded 'jankers' (the origin of the word is unknown but in the armed forces means a restriction of privileges for a minor offence such as being late on duty), Jimmy was ready for a break. When he examined his face in the blurry mirror he used to shave himself in the early mornings, he believed he could see tiny web-like lines forming at the corners of his eyes. Also, lines at the break of his mouth caused by laughing and smiling for the seven weeks since he'd officially enlisted. Now he was going home to be married; Lizzie Prescott wanted to get that ring on her finger before Rocky climbed aboard the ship that would take him to adventures new, and women new!

During his three weeks' embarkment leave, there was a quick wedding on the 27th of August in St Helens followed by a ten-day honeymoon in Dublin, which for 1959 was considered exotic, before Jimmy had to make his way down to Southampton to meet the 'ship', the *Empire Fowey*. It took a train, a taxi, another train and a bus to get him to the dock on time. The embarkation was delayed slightly before the troop ship, full of young, fresh British blood, set sail from Southampton docks on the 7th of October 1959.

Summer 1959 in England was becoming known for its longevity rather than breaking any record temperatures, but on the Wednesday morning the sun shone brightly over Southampton, reaching 21 degrees centigrade. That made it the warmest place in the UK that year for the number of times that benchmark was attained. Rocky, Ginger and Jock waved forlornly at the handful of people dockside who waved them off, none of whom they knew. Two weeks later and the voyage simply wasn't turning into the high-seas adventure they had all hoped for and, simply put, the lads were bored for most of their waking hours.

Rocky was sat with his two muckers, a term for best friend that came from the mines. Anyone who mopped your brow for you at the pit face, as it was too cramped to do it yourself with a hammer in one hand and a chisel in the other, was your mucker, and hence your best friend. They had played cards, smoked, already reminisced of home and the comforts they had taken for granted, and Rocky had even had his first taste of jankers.

He foolishly waited for a mate to finish fastening his boots and was late on deck. Eighteen large buckets of peeled potatoes later, he started to understand the expression, 'Everyone for themselves', and vowed not to let anyone make him late again. They all gambled but were slowly acclimatising themselves to exactly how much the shilling in the pocket of their army fatigues was worth to them.

The basic pay for a private soldier was thirty-eight shillings or £1.90 a week. This compared very unfavourably with the average weekly wage at the time of approximately fifteen pounds, ten shillings or £15.50 a week, a weekly reduction of £13.60 or eighty-eight per cent. But the men didn't have anything to spend their thirty-eight shillings or 'bob', the slang term for shillings, on. All board and food were provided, so it was ciggies, betting, saving to send home or saving for shore leave. They had to get used to a much higher value of currency.

Sometimes, the low wages were further reduced by deductions for lost or damaged kit and equipment. Basically, National Servicemen often had little money left for social activities beyond a visit to the navy, army and air force institutes, known as the NAAFI, to drink subsidised beer. So, Rocky and his two best muckers were sat looking out to sea. Jock said,

"I'm off for a walk round the deck. Anyone coming?" From the two grunts he received in reply, he assumed not and went on his merry way. Along with a couple of hundred of other new servicemen doing exactly the same thing, he trundled around the deck. Ginger and Rocky sat in silence, pulling on their smokes. The sea was a slate grey and relatively calm as they crossed the Mediterranean, with the occasional slap of a wave the only natural sound to be heard, coupled with the shouts of men playing various deck games of their own design. The grey of the sea was offset with the dazzling serene blue of the sky with nary a high cloud breaking across the horizon to end the monotony. Ginger and Rocky were hypnotised into their respective silences.

Twenty minutes later, Jock, who whenever was met for the first time always had to explain why someone with a relatively posh northern English accent had picked up the nickname Jock, slunk back next to his comrades.

"Nice walk?" asked Rocky.

"You'll be surprised to hear that the view east, west and north is pretty much the same as the view south."

Ginger chose to join in the conversation.

"Do you two never shut up?" he asked. "I'm trying to get a little shut-eye here."

"Pardon me for breathing, you big lump," reposted Jock.

Jesus, thought Rocky. *Here we go again.* Now, Jock was never going to be a match for the sheer physicality that Ginger brought to any disagreement, but he never took a backward step either, disregarding all safety for his own body. His mantra for life was a simple one of three words: 'Take No Shit!' And, true to himself and his mantra, he never did, which meant matching up to Ginger's less than 'Live and let live' approach to life. Somewhere in the middle of all this sat Rocky, basically trying to manage his way through the National Service process with as little hassle as possible and get back to his new bride, Lizzie, in one piece. As it happened, he played peacemaker to Jock and Ginger, but neither would do the other any actual harm, and when it came to anyone else then it would be these Three Musketeers versus all comers. They had bonded quickly into an uneasy alliance, helped as they shared the three- tier bunk beds required to fit all the troops onto the boat. As you may have surmised, Ginger was on top, with Rocky in the middle and Jock on the bottom, which summed up their relationship perfectly.

Ginger would, under any other circumstances, have taken being called a big lump as a considered slur on his masculinity, but as he opened his eyes to tell Jock to 'stick it where the sun doesn't shine', something flashed before his eyes. Then it happened again and before he could open his mouth to speak, several more silver flashes erupted from the water before vanishing again into the depths. They had all seen them and the three jumped up from their reverie and grabbed the metal rails in front of them, as did every soldier on that side of the ship.

The troops were amazed, having never seen anything like it before. Within seconds, the air was full of flying and leaping fish.

"Look at them," said Rocky. "Their fins are like proper little wings. Look at that one closest, it's out the water for ages. It's really flying."

Ginger added, "Look at the big one in the middle. He's staying up for ages. He'll beat yours, Rocky, you watch." Within seconds, Ginger's fish was submerged again and Rocky's was still skimming away on the surface.

"Oh, I like that little one there," said Jock. "Its skin is that bright with the sun, it's flashing at us." Everyone was laughing and cheering and had found something to quell the boredom. Jock was the first to suggest it and then everyone was doing it.

"I'll bet you a ciggie my little one beats yours, Rocky."

"I'll take that bet," said Ginger before Rocky had a chance to speak, "and I'll take that one at the head of the four." As quickly as the flying fish had appeared, glistening and reflecting both off the sea and the sun like mirrors flashing across the surface of the water, bets were being laid on which fish could fly the furthest or stay out of the water for longest. It was the most fun the troops had had in the first two weeks of the voyage. It was exhilarating, and long after the fish had taken a different course and moved out of sight, the young men continued to talk about them late into the night.

The journey was to be as follows: Southampton; Gibraltar; along the north coast of the African continent before cutting through the Suez Canal and stopping off at Aden in the Yemen; on to Columbo in Ceylon; Singapore, before docking in Hong Kong. The journey would take from the 7th of October and all things being well would mean arrival in Hong Kong around a month later on the 7th of November.

The following day, after seeing the flying fish, the ship got to the Suez Canal. On its approach to the canal entrance, the ship had to weave its way in and out of the shipwrecks from the 1956 war. The ship slowed to a virtual standstill in order to avoid the wreckage and the men on ship fell silent out of respect for the fallen seamen that had gone before them. There were more than forty ships sunk in order to make access to the canal impassable.

Ginger asked the question many were too frightened to ask for fear of being humiliated. "What exactly happened here? Why does this Nasser bloke hate us all?"

Rocky knew. Something he had always been interested in was current affairs, especially when it came to warfare and politics. Several men gathered round to hear what he had to say.

"It was called the Sinai War in Israel. They invaded Egypt to try and get control of this very canal we're about to go through. And they wanted to get rid of 'that Nasser bloke', as Ginger called him. His full name is Gamal Nasser and he'd taken the canal as his own, or his country's own, and nationalised it under Egypt."

"How do you know all this bollocks?" encouraged Ginger.

Rocky took his life in his hands and replied. "Something you won't know much about, Ginge. It's called R E A D I N G." Rocky stretched the word out for comic effect and luckily on this occurrence, Ginger laughed as well, prompting everyone else to laugh, even if it was with an exhale of breath.

"Anyway, the canal was actually owned by British and French businessmen even though it was originally built by Egyptian and Frenchie governments. When I say businessmen, I mean our government bought lots of shares in the canal. So, us and the Frenchies sent our lads in. Then the Russians and Yanks got involved, saying we shouldn't have sent troops in, so we withdrew, the canal got shut by Nasser and to a certain extent we were humiliated on the world stage. It was about three years ago. Do you remember, Anthony Eden eventually resigned as prime minister over it all?"

There were wise nods from the men stood around Rocky.

Salford Dave – there were many Davids on board, and so recognition came through geography – asked Rocky, "So, what were all those wrecks we just came through, Rocky?"

"Well, just before the Egyptians were defeated – They weren't really a match for British, French and Israeli troops, which is why I think the rest of the world took issue – Just before they were beat, they sunk a load of ships so that no one could use the canal. What you see now is after they've all been moved so we can get through again."

Cleggy, another better-read individual than the ship average, added, "The real reason we got in bother about it was it became clear afterwards that Israel, France and Britain had got together to plan out the invasion. It wasn't just a reaction from us as to what Israel was doing. That's why Eden had to go."

Once again, the members of the *Empire Fowey* jury nodded their unanimous assent.

Ginger again. "Who's in charge now then? Is it Nasser?"

Rocky replied. "It's really complicated now, and I don't understand all of it, but essentially, yes, Nasser has his canal back, but the United Nations have what they call peacekeepers, to look after the borders. When we get to Port Said, which won't be long now, we'll stop, but none of us will be allowed off. Not safe for us with these uniforms on. That's as much as I know, lads."

Rocky didn't realise it immediately, but his estimation had risen many levels in his ability to command the attention of a group of men and to keep them interested in a subject that many of them didn't have an interest in. He was helped by the fact that the recent history was all around them and still very much alive. The men disbanded slowly, returning to their own 'spots' on deck where their stake had been previously claimed.

Jock, who had been silent throughout but had been listening intently, said to Rocky, "You might have started this journey with skin like milk but you're a dark horse. Cleverer than you look."

"He has to be," chuckled Ginger. Quite a funny joke for someone whose sense of humour had been extracted during his childhood years.

After a short stay in Port Said, with no shore leave, as predicted by Rocky, the ship made its way through the canal that had thrown up so much political upheaval in the previous three years and would, unbeknownst to the servicemen, continue to do so for years into the future. The men had amused themselves by throwing pennies off the ship into the water and watching the local children dive down into the deep to retrieve them. A further opportunity for bets to be made and ciggies to be won and lost.

Private A***** H*****. Royal Army Medical Corps – "I was very conscious of the fact that there was no way that I could ever have hoped to visit any foreign country without the assistance of the queen."

The calendar and the nautical miles moved forward until on the 27th of October, the *Empire Fowey* docked in the Ceylon port of Columbo. The difference this time was that for the first time in twenty days, 'the Likely Lads' from the north-west of England would be getting shore leave. Woe betide anyone who got in their way!

Christleton, Cheshire

2019

Anne Smith, an ordinary name for an ordinary person, living in a small English town with an unusual name, Christleton, meaning 'Christ's Little Town' or 'Christian's Farm', depending on which historian takes your fancy. It was two miles from Chester, Cheshire, but had been in existence in some form since the Domesday Book in 1086 when it was referenced as Christetone.

Anne was tall, lanky even. As if in some way she was in synchrony with a tall wading bird's gait, she took long strides when she walked but bringing her knees up too high, slightly, like she was a giant string puppet with an exaggerated walk. There was no fat on her, or if there was, it was well hidden, and her clothes hung slightly off her shoulders and hips as if everything she wore was half a size too large. She opted for loose-fitting summer dresses, even when it was too cold, or baggy light blouse and full skirt combinations in pastel colours. She suited hats but saved them for special occasions, like when someone was born, married, or died. The triumvirate of signposts that signalled most people's lives. Most people she knew anyway.

She wasn't born Anne Smith; she was born Anne Holmes, but the 'Institution' decreed it right and proper she become a Smith after a trip down the aisle. She preferred her old name; she always felt that was who she was, Anne Holmes. A name with character. She loved Colin but truly didn't want to be a Smith. THE most popular surname in the English language, but she went along with it because that's what she did most of her life; she went along with things. Things being decisions, children, house moves, work suggestions, even what to eat for dinner; she wore her pastels and made good.

She was a primary school teacher and had been since leaving college. Colin was a banker. The girls, Eve and Sofia, had graduated university with degrees in Sociology and Literature and now both worked in retail until they could work out what they really wanted to do. One thing they both did know was they wanted to move away from their childhood home and in with their respective boyfriends. So, Anne was an empty nester, but her work turned her into a secondary mother every weekday of the year and she loved it.

Her school kids depended on her and as she caught her own eye in the window of Top Shop, she knew she depended as much on them. Colin was a banker but worked for a large Swiss bank that called on him on a regular basis to get the earliest flight imaginable from Manchester Airport and kidnapped him away to wonderful destinations that he never had the opportunity to explore. They both kept their heads down and made good. That's what you did: you were born, you married, you made good, and you died. As a self-help book, it wasn't going to become a bestseller.

Top Shop, Chester. Anne popped in. Something had caught her eye in the window as she glanced in. It was either that beautiful paisley dress (yes, paisley was making its umpteenth comeback), or it was the faded reflection of herself, and there, trapped right in the corner of her eye, it was her life passing her by. She decided it was the dress as she couldn't cope with not coping today and the thought of the passage of her life and its meaning to the wider world. Ten minutes later, she popped out again with the dress; yet another dress. Unfortunately, she didn't have any particular event where she could wear it.

She loped back to her car and set off for her big house in Christleton that most people would never be either lucky or hardworking enough to aspire to. But now that the girls had gone, the house was simply too big. Thursday night, Colin away in Paris (*Oh, it's simply terrible here on my own, love*), the girls busy having lives, an INSET day next day at school and Anne with a Marks and Spencer dinner for one, along with a cheap bottle of wine, a new dress and a recording of last night's *Sewing Bee*.

Christleton, playground of the rich and famous, population 2,053.

She would ring Mum later; she had been on her own since Dad passed away a couple of years ago. Her two brothers lived miles away, Graham and David, both down south somewhere near the sea; not that either swam much, they just liked living near it. In fact, Graham went on holiday to Barbados once and they had to change the name of the activity to 'Sinking with Turtles'.

Later, she woke up on the couch after two-thirds of a bottle of wine. She had a set time for ringing Mum but every time she dialled, she got a little more annoyed that her brothers didn't pick the phone up more often to Mum. Luckily, they were both with two good women, not two each, who made sure that they talked to Mum at least twice a week. After all, she was in her eighties now and although she had Louise, a black poodle, as company, loved speaking to her kids, especially about her beloved rugby league and cricket. Anne was more a football fan herself but supported Everton, so got little joy from that pastime.

"All right, how's it going? What did you do today?" This tended to be her opening gambit on most calls.

"Hold on a minute, Anne, let me turn the telly down. Hold on, where's the button box? Louise, have you had it?"

"Has she been watching *Scooby Doo* again, Mum? You spoil that dog."

"What? Wait a minute. What did you say about the loo?"

"Not the loo, Mum, Scooby Doo. Never mind, find the button box."

"Got it, got it. Bloody hell, that's loud."

"Mum, you're turning it up, not down. Press mute."

"I'm not a deaf mute. Don't you be so cheeky."

Anne held her head in her hands and if she hadn't been laughing, would have shed tears.

"No, Mum, I said put the telly on mute."

"I'll put it on mute then I can hear what you're saying. There, that's better."

Anne persisted in a very loud voice.

"Have you got your hearing aid in and, before you answer, is it turned on?"

"No, I took it out to answer the phone. It hurts when I press the hearing end against my ear. Wait a minute. I'll put it back in but I can't hold it tight against my ear so I might not be able to hear you very well."

Anne waited as patiently as she could and took another hefty slug of her wine and eventually their conversation got under way. Same as most other days, it was just a ten-minute catch-up. Invariably, they were both on their own. Mother and daughter, sharing the day's mundanities but also hearing a loving voice. Anne was a good listener, but she had to be as her mum, née Lizzie Prescott, was a good talker. Nevertheless, Anne did tell her mum that she was feeling a little lost at the moment. Too much time spent in her own company or that of seven-year-olds.

"You need a hobby, you do," Lizzie suggested.

"But what, Mum, what do I start now at fifty-five? I read but I'm not a great reader and unless I join a book club that's a solitary pursuit anyway. I can't imagine turning up to something resembling a self-help group for some addiction and talking about the latest Booker Prize winner. It's just not me."

"There's nothing wrong with a solitary pursuit if it keeps you interested and you believe it's worthwhile. I'm not suggesting you do something for the sake of doing it. Do you still go to that gym?"

"I've stopped the membership; it just wasn't worth it. It was working out, like, £50 for every mile I ran. I run in the park and around the village now, but that's three times a week for thirty minutes."

The phone went dead at either end as both of them paused to think. Lizzie continued pushing her daughter, who, to be fair, she thought needed to stop feeling sorry for herself.

"What about the local college in Chester? There's all sorts of night-school courses you could do there. Graham's Jayne did a pottery course and loved it."

"I know, I agree. I've just got to find something that really interests me or there's no point. I thought 'Creative Writing' might be something I could do, but that becomes too much like hard work. I wasn't a fan of writing essays when I was back in school, and it's got to be something that I want to do, or the added pressure will just stress me even more." Anne's voice was taking on a plaintive tone as she regressed to a child moaning to her mum about homework.

Lizzie had one more go with her daughter before calling it a night and going back to the paused and muted *Coronation Street* episode she'd been watching since 1961 – not the same episode, the same programme, although Anne suggested it may as well be the same episode.

"What about that thing Colin got you for your last birthday, that blood thing? You've never done that."

"That's three years ago now, Mum. I don't even know where it is. Don't worry yourself. I'm just feeling a bit sorry for myself. I'll be okay. Goodnight."

"Goodnight, love," and Lizzie put the phone down on her daughter.

Anne sighed and dropped the black plastic phone into its cradle. She smiled and thought how well her mum was doing. She would be eighty next year and, while a little hard of hearing, still drove herself around as long as there was no motorway driving involved; she managed all her appointments online with 'her tablet'; she had her own Facebook profile and loved seeing all the photos of her grandkids and great-grandkids; she used Amazon like it was going out of fashion and saw a wide group of friends through a 'Friends Reunited' group and a scrabble club. She was doing really well for someone living on her own and approaching her eighty-first year.

She smiled to herself as she recollected a story about her mum. Dad had been alive then and they had driven down to stay with Graham, Jayne and the kids for a couple of days. Graham loved his movies and television series and was always one of the first in the queue when either innovative technology or a new viewing experience came out.

Their mum and dad had been watching *Coronation Street* at Graham's and he'd just got Sky Plus, with all the gadgetry that came with it. Dad got up to make a cup of tea at half-time but wasn't back in the living room in time, so Graham, using the new function of Sky Plus, paused the live television programme.

You could almost see the words roll across his mum's face: *What sorcery is this?*

"What have you done, Graham? Why's the screen frozen?"

"I've paused it, Mum. It's new from Sky. You can now pause live programmes."

Anne laughed out loud as she remembered what Graham had told her had been Mum's response.

"What about next door? What if they're watching *Coronation Street*? They're not going to be happy with you pausing it for them." Even Dad was amazed when he got back in the room. Dad, gone a couple of years now. Anne's thoughts continued to flit about as is the way when you're sat on your own for hours at a time. *Wonder what he would make of all the streaming everyone does now.*

Then she thought about her birthday present from a couple of years ago. The company was called Hereditary. They offered you the opportunity to trace your ancestry from a drop of blood. If she could find that present, the box was in a wardrobe somewhere, probably in one of the girls' rooms, would she go through with it? Now that she was interested, you could rest assured Graham and David would be as well. Dad would never let them when he was alive but what if, just what if, what if she could find out what really happened all those years ago. Because none of them knew for sure!

Hampton, London

1977–78

Mary was worried about Uncle Ted. She also worried about Bert, who worked for the council. He'd picked up a trade in the navy; it's just that no one could put a name to it. Bit of this, bit of the other, he used to say, but he'd been made a foreman as he didn't suffer fools gladly and led by example. You might say he ran a tight ship, especially after his time in the navy. Mary also ran a tight ship around the house, and it was always spotless, plus Bert's dinner was always ready when he walked through the door from work. That's what she had always done and that's what she always would do. In their household, there was, she believed, a fair distribution of labour. Bert worked and got paid and she worked at home and didn't.

She was also worrying about her daughter Jayne's O-level results, due next week on the 25th of August, a Thursday. Jayne had to be in school for 10am and she would get handed a little slip of paper on which would be the road map for at least the next two years of her life and a long-term plan for her full career. That was the level of importance that Mary placed on the results. She wanted Jayne, their only child, to have a chance at the career that she had never had. When younger, she'd worked as a bookkeeper for a while but only because she was 'good with figures', no formal training required in those days.

In 1977, everything was opening up for working-class people to get on in life, make something of themselves, and if Jayne got to university, she would be the first Church or Johnson ever to do so. Hence, Mary worried, but it was her default setting. Everything had its own little box in her head and needed ticking off. Not once either; she liked to come back on a regular basis to the storeroom in her head, recheck the contents of each box, undertake a stock take and then a quality control analysis until the box could be ticked again.

The box marked Uncle Ted never retained its 'pass' certificate for very long before being reopened and examined before being repacked until needed again. Chemotherapy in 1977 was in its infancy and made Ted worse before better before worse again. All through his illness during the summer Mary had cooked and cleaned while Bert had gardened and maintained. Ted was in the best hands possible from a friend's perspective, but lung cancer is an uneasy bedfellow and rarely left Ted alone.

Jayne's results came through and, as expected, there had been little to worry about on that front. Several A's, a couple of C's and the rest were B's. No fails, all passes, ten O-levels in all. Off to sixth form college in September to start her A-level courses in Maths, Economics and Business Studies. Life for

Jayne was just starting as life for Uncle Ted was drawing to a close in a painful, undignified manner.

Initially, the chest pains concerned him because he thought he might have heart problems, which caused him to smoke more, which made him think he had heart problems, and so began the vicious mental circle that added to the increased physical pain. He noticed that when he laughed or coughed the pain worsened or, the word he used, deepened. It was as if something was gripping his lungs and squeezing them so he couldn't get his breath in. After diagnosis, he stopped worrying about his heart. He accepted that his heart would win in a race with his lungs to the finishing line.

By the start of October, he had accepted the advice given by the cancer specialists and stopped the chemotherapy. His shortness of breath was worsening, his voice was always hoarse, and he coughed and wheezed continuously. Weakness and fatigue were his constant companions and he spent increased time in bed rather than out of it. Nevertheless, he wanted to stay at home and asked Mary and Bert if they would look after him during what he now knew were going to be his final months.

"Of course we will," said Mary through held-back tears. "I wouldn't have it any other way."

"Don't worry about the garden, Ted. I can look after it while you stay as well as you can," helped Bert. No one suggested Ted was going to get better; their friendship and respect for each other was too strong to pretend at this stage of life, and they didn't want to insult each other's intelligence. So, the vigil started, and the routine worked through October into early November.

Bert arranged with his manager that he would work the continuous 6am until 2pm shift. Mary would rise with him early, and her first chore of the day was to let herself into Ted's and see how his night had been. She would then grab a quick bite to eat for herself after Bert had gone off to work, and see if Ted could keep anything down. Every other day, the doctor would arrive to check Ted's vitals.

"Still here, Doc. Waking up is always a bonus these days," joked Ted. He was, in fact, afraid. Frightened of falling to sleep wondering if the next one might be his last. Mary would then run a vacuum around, even though it wasn't needed most days, see if Ted wanted to get dressed, sit him up in a chair if he could, normally in front of the TV, and then nip back home to settle to her own household chores.

She would go back in with lunch for her and Ted, even if he hardly ate, and go through the ritual of taking lunch with a 'nice cup of tea'. The doctor said the more normal and regular the routine, the better for Ted's state of mind. With the increased quantity and concentration of drugs, Ted was more liable to lapse into confused thoughts and have to endure what the ghosts of the past tried to bring into the present.

Bert would jump on his pushbike at 2pm on the dot and cycle back as quickly as he could. He would only take a detour if they needed fresh vegetables from his allotment. He would then help maintain Ted's garden, which in November was readying it for the winter months rather than keeping growth under control, before Mary and Bert would sit and eat their evening meal with Ted, even if Ted himself was eating less and less.

At some point of the evening, depending on how well Ted was feeling, Mary and Bert would retire to their own residence after ensuring Ted was set for the night. Even with his fatigue, lack of sleep and loss of appetite, he would still be capable of getting himself up in the night if he needed, plus he had the added security of the phone by his bedside that would have Mary and Bert there in a moment if really required. That was the routine that went on through November and December and into the new year of 1978.

January 1978 was a month with a wide variety of weather across the UK ranging from tornadoes to thunderstorms, freezing fog to severe gales, storm surges to blizzards. Heathrow, five miles from Hampton, had snow seven times in January, but Ted wasn't going to see the last snowfall. Through December and early 1978, his symptoms had worsened. He now regularly coughed up blood; his muscles had weakened to the extent that he barely moved from his bed; his blood pressure and blood sugars were through the roof; seizures would grip him; and his confusion was to the extent that he referred to Mary as Lily on many occasions, whoever she may be from Ted's confused mind.

The 20th of January came around and Mary had hardly slept in her own bed that year. The nurse came every day now and Ted was on a drip, although Mary didn't really understand what he was being fed through it. Ted had moments of lucidity but was close to becoming comatose, and her role now was that of hand holder and mouth wiper. The nurse suggested to Mary that today may well be the last sunrise that Ted would see, through the freezing blizzard.

It was 1pm and Bert wasn't due back until 2.30pm, the

soonest he could make it cycling through the horrendous weather conditions outside. Ted hadn't spoken since Tuesday and today was Friday. Mary asked the nurse, "How long has he got, love? My husband will want to see him before he goes."

"He could literally go any minute, Mary. Can you get in touch with Bert?"

"No, he'll be out in the sheds today. There'll be no call for being outside in this weather." She turned and spoke to Ted. "You hang on there, Ted. Bert's coming to see you."

Nurse Wilson left the room to fetch something from her car and noticed that the snow was easing up, as was the wind. She thought to herself, *Thought this was in for the day*. Back in Ted's dining room, where the ward bed from the hospital had been set up, Mary let the first tear of the day wind its way down her tired face.

"Stay with me, Ted, stay with me." Mary realised that Bert wasn't going to get back home from work in time. There was no phone in the sheds, and it had to be life or death for someone to get a message from the council offices to the sheds. This *was* life and death, but the rules were quite specific. It had to be a close blood relative to send someone with a message to 'Get yourself home'.

One thing Ted had always said was, "Make sure you two are there when the time comes. I don't want to be on my own. You two are the best friends I've ever had and there's something nice in the will for you. Just make sure you're sat here to wave me off."

In the council sheds, the lads doing odd jobs on the lathes and generally tidying up, as much as they ever did tidy up, looked out of the grimy windows and saw the change in the sky. The boards holding the shed together and bearing the full brunt of the eastern wind stopped rattling against each other, and Bert's head thrust out of the gate like a turtle from its shell. His wispy hair caught the wind, but it wasn't blowing anything like it was before. He instinctively turned to his wards and said, "I'm knocking off early. Somebody wants me home."

He arrived at Ted's at 1.45pm after a hair-raising churn through what was still quite deep snow. People who saw him that day charging down Teddington High Street with his coat tails flapping behind him like a crow taking flight said that if Bert had been physically capable of breaking a world record that day, then he would have done just that.

Mary turned as Bert shuffled into the room, literally cap in hand, dragging lumps of blackened snow on his shoes with him from the grubby streets.

"I think he's gone, Bert. You've just missed him. He doesn't know anything anyway now."

Bert said what he always said to Ted: "All right, mate, how you doing?"

Ted opened his eyes for the last time and said his final words: "Not too bad, mate. I'll see you later." And then he went, and the snow started falling again outside within seconds and the eaves of the house rattled as the wind picked up.

Mary thought aloud, "It's as if he was waiting for you, Bert." Then came the tears.

Burnley, Lancashire

1936

Elsie had yet to tell Mrs Dawson that she was going out at 6.30pm on Saturday night. It was now 5.30pm on the very day and the hour was approaching. She just had to have the conversation, or the time would come and go when she needed to leave. It was a warm sunny afternoon, and with the Shuttleworths gone for the day, including an overnight stay, there was a swell of good cheer amongst the staff of Gawthorpe Manor as they dragged chairs out of the back door and sat in the late afternoon sunshine. Now was the time to speak to Mrs Dawson.

Mrs Dawson rose from her chair, red in the face from the sun, and puffed her way down the stone steps to the kitchen.

"Time for a cuppa," she said. Elsie followed as quickly as the master's dog follows him from a room.

"Mrs Dawson, can I have a word?" squeaked Elsie. She wasn't begging yet, but her voice lacked authority and came out plaintively. "You sit down. I'll put the kettle on."

Cook shouted from outside, "One for me and Mr Dawson as well."

Elsie quickly filled the kettle and got it onto the stove as Mrs Dawson sat at the large kitchen table where they took the servant meals together.

"Go on then, spit it out. I can tell from your voice you want something."

Elsie took a position a few feet in front of her elder and placing and clasping her hands behind her back, so she didn't get too demonstrative, asked the all-important question. "Mrs Dawson, I wondered awfully if you wouldn't mind if I went down to the town tonight to go to the cinema?" Elsie didn't know why she said awfully, she had never used that word in her life, or why she said cinema instead of flicks, but she did!

"I wondered when you was going to ask me," replied the housekeeper. Elsie was knocked backwards and did, in fact, step back involuntarily.

"I-I-I didn't think you knew," she stammered. "In fact, how do you know?" Elsie wondered exactly what Mrs Dawson had found out.

"I will not allow you to go, my girl, especially after all the efforts you've gone to, to hide the facts, deceive me and make your arrangements."

Elsie could feel her lip trembling, but with anger as much as sadness. Mrs Dawson continued.

"I will not allow you to go unless... There are a few stipulations for you and me to agree first or you don't go."

"Whatever you say, Mrs Dawson." Elsie's cool had evaporated as quickly as drying paint in the noonday sun.

"Firstly, you need to know that Mrs Shacklady and I have been playing bridge together for years."

"Mrs Shacklady?" queried Elsie.

"The telephone switchboard operator in the village."

"Oh yes," said Elsie. "I was only—."

"My advice is to say nothing more if you want to go to the cinema," advised the head housekeeper.

"You rang a garage in Burnley, left a message. Mrs Shacklady rang me, left a message. I spoke to Cook, who spoke to Dot, and she gave Cook a message and then Cook told me the message. The stipulations are as follows.

"One, you pay for the call you made on the Shuttleworths' phone. Mrs Shacklady will be able to tell me how much the call cost. Two. You will be accompanied to the cinema this evening by Dot, and you do not give her a tough time. The girl is feeling terrible as it is that she 'betrayed' you to Cook. At least I know I'm doing right by your mother by providing a chaperone. Thirdly, you do not lie to me again. When I was first told, my immediate thought was to dismiss you with no pay. Making that phone call was stealing and you would never work again if I sacked you. You have two people to thank for the fact that you are being dealt with so leniently. Cook and Mr Dawson. They both persuaded me that you were a good-natured, industrious girl that was away from home and to date had not set a foot wrong.

"Elsie Scott, this is your one and only chance. If you want to make arrangements to see 'men' in the village…" the word men was delivered as though Mrs Dawson had bitten into an apple and found half a maggot "…then you need to tell me the truth. Sometimes, I will say no, because it won't be convenient, but I won't say no out of spite. I reiterate. This is your last and only chance.

"Do you understand, Elsie?" During this monologue, Elsie had gone through every emotion possible. Anger had turned to shame. She had never thought for a second that making a phone call could or would be classed as stealing; she'd never stolen anything in her life. Shame had become terror; the thought that she may have lost her job and had to go home, well, the thought itself was unbearable. Terror had become relief when she realised that she wasn't going to be sacked. Relief had become joy as she understood that 'Cinderella would go to the ball', or at least the flicks. Finally, her joy was short-lived and turned to bewilderment as she realised Cinderella would have to take 'Buttons' along to her date as a sidekick in the form of Dot.

The overwhelming emotion, though, was one of gratitude. She had underestimated Mrs Dawson in so many ways and now had to prove herself all over again, but she knew she could do this. These emotions flashed through her head in seconds, and she said, "Mrs Dawson, I don't have the words to express my gratitude for you giving me this one last chance. Thank you for your wisdom and guidance, I will not let you down again."

"A bit over the top but those words will do. Now go and get yourself ready and take Dot with you. And remember, leave Dot alone. I'll know if you give her bother."

Elsie just nodded and ran off to find Dot.

"Dot, you're coming to the flicks with me. Get dressed into something presentable and be quick about it." The fourteen-year-old girl wasn't sure she understood; in fact, she was quite certain she didn't understand.

"What do you mean, going to the flicks? One, I have no money, and two, you are going with yer fancy fella. You don't want me there."

"What I want at this moment doesn't even enter into it," replied Elsie. "The fact is, Mrs Dawson has said the only way I can go is if you come with me. A sort of chaperone, like. So, put whatever you have fit to wear on and let's get going. James will have to pay for you." The two girls, one only slightly older than the other, scrambled around their small bedroom, throwing clothes around like leaves in an autumn wind.

Eventually, they both wore what they would have worn for church on a sunny Sunday summer's morning; pretty and slight dresses with floral prints, berets and flat shoes.

"Look at us," said Dot. "We look like two Bette Davises."

"More like Joe and Fred Davis, the snooker players, but it'll have to do. I don't have much else apart from work clothes. Come on, let's go. Follow me." Instead of leaving by the servants' door at the back of the manor, Elsie scooted back into the shadowed darkness of the main hall and up the stairs to Lady Shuttleworth's dressing room. Dot, frightened to death of getting caught (Elsie knew because Dot told her so several times), followed with a whimper rather than 'into the breach'.

Elsie said, "You take the green bottle and I'll take this pink one." She then gave herself a liberal dowsing with her ladyship's parfum. "Go on, Dot, have a go." Dot looked terrified so Elsie picked up the other bottle and sprayed Dot, who tried to duck and veer out of the way.

"Okay, out the side door so we can shout our goodbyes. They'll smell us a mile away now."

The house was full of exits and entrances as well as the main majestic double front door, so the girls nipped out through the conservatory, on the west so it faced the river, and shouted to the others sat by the kitchen door.

"See you later, have to run or we'll be late. It's half six now!"

Cook shouted back to them, "You two behave yourselves."

Even Mrs Dawson said, "Have a suitable time."

Mr Dawson said nothing and the lads from the grounds just cheered and jeered until Mr Dawson shut them all up with an old-fashioned look. The girls disappeared around the corner of the house and made their way to the drive and the walk to the High Street.

Dot asked, "Does your fella know I'm coming?"

"He's not me fella," exclaimed Elsie, although she did like the sound of it. "And I'm not even sure if he knows *I'm* coming."

"Well, it's been a lot of faff if he doesn't turn up." Dot was nothing if she wasn't straight talking.

"I know it's been a lot of faff. It almost cost me my job, but it's taught me a lesson. I was accused of stealing because I made a phone call without paying for it, so I've got to be really careful now. I didn't even think it was stealing."

"We've both just taken some of her ladyship's perfume. Do you not think that's stealing?"

Elsie was genuinely startled. *Bloody hell*, she thought, *after promising myself that I'd never take anything again that wasn't mine, I last all of twenty minutes before it happens*

65

again. As the two girls are having this discussion, they wend their way down the long drive with Dot almost having to walk/run to stay abreast of Elsie.

"Dot, I'm not lying when I say this, but I just didn't think borrowing a squirt of perfume was classed as stealing."

"Some old relation of mine got hung for taking a crust of bread."

Elsie spluttered, "Thanks, Dot. Don't ever let me ask you to cheer me up. Well, we can't get caught this time. We will just have to scrub with carbolic before anyone smells us. It might have worn off by then with cigarettes and what have you."

Dot went silent for a moment before slyly looking up at Elsie and saying, "I never touched anything anyway. You sprayed yourself and then you sprayed me."

Elsie needed to nip this in the bud.

"You have it on you, same as I do. If you say anything, you'll get in as much trouble as I will. My advice to you is enjoy your trip to the cinema and say nowt. I'm a better friend than I am an enemy."

Dot backpedalled that far and that quickly that she was almost back at the manor.

"Oh, I don't want to make an enemy, Elsie. I won't say anything, of course I wouldn't. I'm just saying I didn't really do owt wrong. Not really." Elsie let it go, thinking the more they discussed it, the more the seed may be planted in Dot's head to mention it to someone. Elsie wasn't the best at saying the right thing at the right time but compared to Dot, she was the world champion! Elsie changed the subject.

"Do you know what we're going to see, Dot? It's got great reviews and it's been made by a very famous director."

"I've no idea. Half an hour ago, I was going to have a cup of tea and a biscuit and have a gossip with that new stable boy."

"Create some gossip, more likely. Anyway, it's a big Hollywood production called *Mr. Deeds goes to town.*"

Dot harumphed.

"Doesn't sound like a big production. If they made a film of me and you going to town, I don't think many tickets would be sold. *Dot and Elsie go to town and buy some sausages from Burnley High Street.* It's not a catchy title."

Elsie had to laugh, which set Dot off. Elsie had to admit the girl was infectious.

"So, who's in this film and what's it about? It can't just be some bloke going to town?"

Still laughing, Elsie says, "Gary Cooper plays this country yokel who for some reason inherits millions of dollars. Him 'going to town' is him leaving the countryside for a different way of living. Then someone tries to get his money and he falls in love. It's a comedy, but a romantic one. Anyway, it's all that's on so that's what we're seeing."

Dot replies, "Gary Cooper with millions of dollars. The women round here would have to form a queue to get to him. No wonder someone falls in love with him. He's hardly selling tripe at the market, is he?"

The two girls were laughing so hard that they virtually stumbled from the drive of Gawthorpe Hall onto Burnley Road. It was a quarter to seven and they had another ten-minute walk from Burnley Road to where the cinema was on Holmes Street.

Dot asked, "Where are we going exactly?"

"The Empire, off Lune Street. We go right now onto Burnley Road, over the bridge and take a right. It's not far now. We took too long wandering up the drive, laughing like Laurel and Hardy."

"I 'ope they're the short before the main film. I love Laurel and Hardy. I watched that one when they were carrying a piano and wet me knickers, I laughed that much."

"Well, that's something to look forward to then," said Elsie, thinking that this first date had every chance of turning into a nightmare now that it was her, James and the spare leg of Dot. They arrived at a busy Empire. Saturday night was very much movie night in Burnley, which at the time had six or seven busy cinemas dependent upon the availability of one or two church hall cinemas, which only showed movies sporadically. People were coming and going but there was no sign of James Knowles.

"This isn't looking too good for you," said Dot. "I 'ope you've got enough for a ticket for me and you if he's not here." Elsie checked her purse; she had two shillings and with twelve pennies per shilling, that was 24d. It was 10d each to get in, which would leave her with 4d. She should have just enough to buy them both an ice cream. A real treat.

And then there he was.

Elsie looked across at him walking out of the foyer clutching two tickets and a box of chocolates, and she knew she hadn't been absolutely honest with herself. Thinking about the ice cream she was considering buying, she melted herself in the late evening sunshine. She couldn't just throw herself at Mr Knowles, but her tummy tickled her, and her legs felt weak. She may not throw herself, but she may just stumble. Dot didn't help. "Bloody hell, it's Gary Cooper himself." Indeed, James had made an effort; clean white shirt and blue tie, light grey summer suit with the latest pleated trousers and shoes that would be able to warn ships away from a rocky coastline as the sun bounced off them. Dot literally stared, her eyes misting over as if she were looking at a film star or royalty.

Elsie whispered through clenched teeth. "Pull yourself together, Dot. You look like Fay Wray in *King Kong*." The reference was lost on Dot, but she did manage to regain a little dignity, casting her eyes downward as James strolled over.

"Good evening. If it isn't Miss Elsie Scott. I'm so pleased you made it. I got the message and took the liberty of buying us a couple of stall tickets before they all went. I didn't realise you would have a friend with you."

"Neither did I," answered Elsie. "This is Dot, the cook's help. The only way I could come was if she chaperoned me. Housekeeper's orders, I'm afraid. But I'm still very happy to be here." Elsie backed this up with the best smile she had, head up, teeth on display, red lips glistening.

"Okay, you take these," James handed Elsie the tickets and the box, "the chocolates are for you, I hope you like them. Dot, wait here with Elsie and I'll try and get you a ticket before they all go."

James vanished back into the foyer as quickly as he had appeared. Elsie turned to Dot.

"Put your eyes back in, Dot. You'll be making him think 'he's all that', the way you're gawping at him."

"Oh, Elsie, if you don't marry him, I will."

"You daft girl, I've hardly spoken to him yet. Let alone you talking about marrying. Anyway, he's too old for you. I think he might be too old for *me*." The words leaving Elsie's mouth did not match the thoughts in her head: *He's not too old for me at all. In fact, it's the perfect match. Like Douglas Fairbanks and Mary Pickford. He was more than twenty years older than her, and they made it work.* Another part of her brain told her, *You're not in Hollywood, Elsie. You're in Burnley*, but she chose to ignore that part.

Dot answered. "I'll take me chances if you don't."

"Shut up, he's on his way back." Elsie was starting to despair that she'd had to bring Dot with her.

James announced, "Okay, Dot, I've managed to get you a ticket but unfortunately they had none left in the stalls so you're in the circle, but it's a good seat, not too far back and relatively central, so you should have an unobstructed view of Gary Cooper."

It was now that all of Dot's fourteen years came to the surface. She may have had designs on being a young woman with the maturity to be with a man James's age, but she was what she was, a not-long-out-of-school immature young girl. It didn't help that James handed her a Wall's choc ice, like giving sweets to a child to keep them happy. Dot had never had a full choc ice to herself so although she was angry at being shunted away from the adults, she did have a full choc ice to enjoy. They had only been in existence just over ten years and were somewhat of a novelty still, especially to the working classes.

"But Mrs Dawson said I had to stay with Elsie."

Elsie wasn't taking this. She had taken about as much hassle as she could live with on her first-ever proper date, with a real man, not a kid from the narrow streets of St Helens.

"Dot, when Mrs Dawson said I have to bring you along, she obviously did not know that we wouldn't be able to get three seats together. You are lucky that Mr Knowles has agreed to buy you a ticket. And a choc ice. Surely you don't expect one of us two to take the single seat?" In her anger, Elsie had reverted to the formal Mr Knowles rather than James. He actually wondered if he would ever win this girl over enough so she would be comfortable on first-name terms.

James also felt the pressure of volunteering to take the lone ticket in the circle and opened his mouth to speak. Elsie gave him a look that he could only interpret as *Don't you even think about it,* and his mouth snapped shut like the closing of an animal trap set by a poacher.

"James, take me in. Dot, we will meet you here after the film. DO NOT leave on your own." Elsie took the crook of James's arm and led him like a lawyer leading a witness into the cinema. James presented the tickets and moments later they were sat in the dark just as the Pathé newsreel started up with the crowing of a cockerel.

The newsreel was a mixed batch of items that had occurred in the previous couple of months: Reynoldstown won the Grand National for the second time; preparations were well under way for the Berlin Olympics that would take place in August of 1936; Cambridge won the boat race by five lengths; the recently finished *Queen Mary* left Clydebank for Southampton from where she would make her maiden voyage to New York; Edward VIII was having a very public relationship with Wallis Simpson and the Hindenburg made its first flight in Germany.

Elsie wouldn't normally have taken much interest in the news, but she could see that James was fascinated with the flickering black and white newsreel, especially the part about Berlin and the Hindenburg. He turned and whispered in her ear so as not to disturb anyone else, but also so that he could get as close to Elsie as possible. "That Hitler is going to cause trouble, I can tell. He's running rings around Stanley Baldwin." His lips tickled Elsie's ear, but she wouldn't have moved if the Empire had been burning to the ground. She snuggled into him and asked a question, more to show interest rather than with real inquisitiveness.

"What were all the bits of paper falling from the Hindenburg?"

"We don't know for sure," answered James, "but some people believe it's propaganda to preach Hitler's ways to the German public." Elsie didn't really know what propaganda meant but thought better of asking again. The newsreel finished and then there was a short Buster Keaton comedy before the main event. Elsie loved *Mr. Deeds*. It made her laugh; it made her sigh, and she was rooting for Gary Cooper and Jean Arthur to get together, which they subsequently did.

James laughed in all the right places, but he enjoyed watching Elsie enjoy the movie and spent most of the two hours, a long film, watching her rather than the bright screen. Elsie was not immune to his presence and when 'Deeds and Babe' kissed in the courtroom at the end of the film, she leant over and kissed James on the cheek.

"Thank you," she said. James turned to return her kiss with a full-blooded one straight on her red lips, but the lights came up and he retreated like Dracula in the sunshine. From above them came the screech of one Dot, leaning perilously over the balcony rail after leaving her seat and running down the aisle against the crowd.

"Oi, you two, don't think you're Mr Deeds and Babe. Put her down. You don't know where she's been."

If James was thinking of sneaking a quick kiss, even in the light, that chance had gone quicker than Mae West's reputation!

"Come on," he said, "let's meet your crazy friend outside."

Elsie gave him her best smile and said, "I've had a lovely time. Perhaps next time we don't have to bring Dot."

"We could go dancing?" queried James.

"Not this time. Dot won't get in the Towneley Park Dance Hall. She might think she's all grown up, but you have to be twenty-one to get in there. I may not get in!"

"It's not 10pm yet, we could go for a drink?" James was not about to give up.

"What about Dot? I have to get her back to the manor. I won't be able to see you ever again if I mess this up this time."

James had a grin from ear to ear.

Elsie asked, "What's up with you? You look like the cat that's got the cream when I've just told you I have to go."

"Yes, but you said the magic words. 'Next time.'"

They were now stood outside waiting for Dot to get down from the circle. She would be the last out because she had walked to the front of the circle just so she could shout down from up above. Elsie stood on tiptoes and leant in. "Until next time," then she kissed him hard on his lips but kept her mouth firmly closed. This was enough for a first date. Wrong ideas and all.

Dot was watching from inside the cinema doors with

green eyes all a-blazing. She breezed out and Elsie quickly pulled apart from James, thinking they had got away with it and not been seen kissing.

"What a great film," said Dot, "I could watch it all over again. I'll bet you two could as well because you couldn't have seen much with all that canoodling you were doing." She laughed, but the laugh didn't reach her eyes, and James saw, even if Elsie didn't.

James stepped in.

"Come on then, let's get you two home."

"Oh, me feet are killing me," said Dot. "It's a good twenty minutes from here and these are me best flats I've got on. Which means I've hardly used them. Me little toe has bent double under the others on me right foot. Left foot. One of them anyway."

With a smile and a hint of panache, James announced, "You're not walking tonight, ladies. I have a car with me from the showroom. One of the best.

"It's a Morris Eight Series 1 in a beautiful blue colour. Just to match my eyes, Elsie. I've parked it around the corner at the back of the row of cottages."

Elsie was impressed but didn't like the eyes comment. It was for her to admire his eyes; self-admiration counted for nothing as far as she was concerned. Dot was bouncing like a Labrador waiting to chase a stick.

"I've only ever been in one car before and that was when I was little and got knocked over in the street. The man who hit me took me and me mum to the hospital. It was almost worth the broken leg." She was literally bouncing up and down on the spot.

Five minutes later, James was sat behind the wheel of what was undeniably a beautiful piece of engineering. Elsie was sat by his side and Dot was in the back practising waving to those less fortunate than herself. As this was normally nobody in Burnley, she was enjoying the moment, saying, "It's just like one of those cars the gangsters drive and stand on the side of in the films."

James smiled, raised his eyebrows to Elsie and replied, "I'll take you both for a spin."

He then took the two lucky girls around the Burnley countryside, headlights blazing and breaking what speed limits existed in 1936. Dot had wound down the back window and had her head hanging out, looking every inch a deranged poodle as her hair flapped around her head like a pair of errant dog ears. She also screeched an annoying whinnying sound that defied description.

"Shut up, Dot," said Elsie. "You'll attract everyone in the neighbourhood to us."

James took them north then north-east to the village of Higham, then further east to Fence before heading cross-country across to Nelson. He then headed south through Pendle Village and Brierfield before getting back onto the Burnley Road and aiming them home to Gawthorpe Manor. Elsie had to admit that it was exhilarating. As he headed up the driveway, James stayed in a low gear and just kept his sidelights on to keep the noise down and attract as little attention as possible to themselves.

Dot had quietened down and slumped back on the hard leather seats in the back, window now firmly closed. No one in the car spoke as their fifteen-minute adventure around the Lancashire countryside came to a close. James pulled up at the side of the house out of view from any of the doors or windows used by the staff of the manor. It was quiet, and off to their right an owl hooted in Tipping Hill Wood, approximately a mile to the east of the manor.

Elsie gave Dot her instructions.

"Dot, go to the back door to the kitchen and wait there for me. Do not go in on your own. Please. Just give me two minutes to say good night to James."

For once, Dot did as she was told. James jumped out of the car and opened the door for Dot with a deep bow, as though he was welcoming home the lady of the manor. Dot giggled, said good night and skipped around the side of the manor to the rear. James re-entered the car.

"So, it's time to say good night," he said.

This time, Elsie let James kiss her with a little more passion and she had to pull away to catch her breath.

"Let's do this again, only next time on our own," she said. James nodded in the dark, but Elsie didn't see. "Only if you want to, of course," she added.

He took her hand and held it to his chest. His heart was pounding.

"What does that tell you?" he asked in return.

Elsie paused. "It tells me I have a very amorous beau."

James laughed. "I'll be in touch and don't worry, I'll find a way. If not, you have my number at the garage or you can always walk down to me as I guess you don't want me coming here?"

"Not when the Shuttleworths are home. I don't mind you meeting all the rest of the staff, but I'll have to clear it first.

And now I have to go." She pecked him one last time and leapt from her side of the car before James could play Sir Galahad for the final time that night. Elsie ran off, waving back over her shoulder but without turning around. As she rounded the corner of the manor, she ran straight into Dot, who had been doing her utmost to eavesdrop and spy on Elsie.

"Do you ever do what is asked of you, Dorothy?" Full name required when a telling-off was needed. Dot just laughed like she always did. It was so difficult to be angry with the girl for very long.

They spilled into the kitchen like two burglars picking the lock and finding the door swinging away from them as they broke in. Only Cook and Mrs Dawson were sat at the kitchen table.

"At last, we thought you would never get back," said Cook, trying to stop Mrs Dawson from spoiling the moment for the girls. It was approaching 11pm and that was considered late, probably very late as per Mrs Dawson's timekeeping.

Mrs Dawson surprised them both by saying, "Right, quickly get yourselves a cocoa each and then sit here with me and Cook for ten minutes and tell us all about it." So, Elsie and Dot did just that.

Colombo, Ceylon
(now Sri Lanka)

1959

Rocky, Ginger and Jock were on land again even though it was a land they didn't recognise or understand.

Between 1947 and 1963, a total of 395 National Servicemen were killed on active service.

"Bloody hell, it's warm," exclaimed Jock. The average lowest temperature in Colombo is 24 degrees centigrade or 75 fahrenheit in old money. The average high is 30 degrees C or 86F. This particular day in 1959 it was 33 degrees centigrade. Jock was indeed correct; it was warm.

It also rained every other day as September and October is the rainy season and when it rained in Colombo, it came straight down in such large droplets that if one hit Jock fair and square directly on the crown of his head, Ginger said, "It would knock the little one clean over." Something of an exaggeration but Rocky gave him the benefit of the doubt and laughed anyway. One did tend to laugh at Ginger's jokes for fear of reprisal, but they had become an inseparable threesome over the first few weeks of their service.

Rocky asked, "So, do you know where we're going, Ginge, or is this going to be a wander until we find a bar?"

"Just taking in the sights, Rocky lad. Look at this beautiful harbour. And have you ever seen such blue seawater? And there's a lake in the middle of the city that everyone says you have to see. It's called Beery Lake, so I think that's where we'll go."

Jock's eyes nearly fell out of his head.

"What are you saying, Ginger, a lake made of beer?"

"You daft bugger," said Rocky. "It's Beira Lake. I think named after one of the Dutch engineers who helped make it. You didn't really believe there was a lake made of beer, did you?"

"Course not. Just jesting, mate." Ginger and Rocky looked at each other and burst out laughing.

Ginger said, "You're going to take some stick for that when we tell everyone, Jock."

Jock just pulled a face and muttered an expletive under his breath about sex and travel.

Ginger nevertheless was correct about the harbour being beautiful. One of the suggestions for the origin of the name Colombo came from a so-called tree the natives called *ambo*, which bears the mango fruit, growing around the harbour area, the leaves of which in the Ceylon language was *cola*, and hence they called the tree *colambo*, which the Christians in honour of Columbus turned to Colombo. These trees, still present in 1959, gave the harbour an otherworldly look, as though the trees had parted simply to let the boats and ships glide into dock.

Rocky, still laughing, said, "Come on then, let's find this beer lake. Be careful swimming, though, Jock, as you don't want to get in over your head. Head, get it, Ginger. Head, like on a pint."

Ginger replied, "Hope there's no WH-ales in there." Unfortunately, that was the best Ginger could come up with, and it took a bit of explaining to his two mates where exactly that pun was coming from.

Jock retaliated: "I think you'd better leave the jokes to me and Rocky, eh, Ginger. We don't want you taxing yourself." He jumped out of the way just before the point of Ginger's size twelve army boot caught him right in the crack of his arse.

The three men continued to walk around the harbour front bantering, delighted to be off ship for a few hours. As they were walking along the front before they cut inland to the lake, they came across one of the most famous hotels east of Suez: the Galle Face Hotel on Galle Road. The hotel had been there since 1864 and had a wonderful reputation for tasty food and celebrity guests. Our three intrepid servicemen took one look and thought they'd died and gone to heaven.

"Sweet Jesus, look at that place," said Ginger. "I've always wanted to rock up somewhere like that an' order an ice-cold beer."

"They won't let us three in there," said Rocky.

"Why not?" said Ginger. "We are respectable members of the British Army. Look at that plaque there. It says Prince

Philip stayed here. And look at the picture, he had his uniform on. If it's good enough for Phil, it's good enough for us."

Jock, always one to look after the pennies, asked, "How much is a pint in there, though, Ginger? Can we afford it?"

"Our money will go a long way here. Don't you worry, Jocky boy. Plus, how are they going to stop me? I've not seen anyone over five foot six since I've been here."

Ginger had that determined look on his face.

"The Galle Face Hotel," he read. "Come on, let's go and get our first pint for four weeks." Ginger strode off determinedly, and his two mates trotted by his side to keep up with him down the long drive to the hotel lobby.

The hotel drive swept anticlockwise around to the splendid white façade that overpowered the natural landscape, which had precedent by several thousand years. Three towers, one central with a prominent ornate arched entry, while the other two flanked at either end, defending the middle like two guardsmen protecting the castle gate. Over twenty windows per floor and at least four floors gazed back at the three mates like the closed eyes of a sleeping sentinel. To the right of the hotel and covering the front of the left wing were over twenty majestic palm trees, leaning in different directions like straws dropped loose into a glass tumbler.

"Leave this to me," said Ginger, "I know how to speak to these Ceylon lads." Jock and Rocky glanced at each other as if to say they weren't quite as sure as Ginger was.

The hotel was originally built by four British entrepreneurs in 1864. Its name derived from the stretch of lawn which it faces, known as the Galle Face Green, and it began life as a Dutch villa called Galle Face House. Land for the hotel's expansion was purchased between 1870 and 1894, and architect Edward Skinner completed the design of the hotel's south wing, which still exists. It has remained largely unchanged until the present day, though with many extensive restorations, but in 1959 was very much still in prime condition.

The hotel also employed the world's oldest hospitality industry veteran and doorman, Kottarapattu Chattu Kuttan or KC. He joined the hotel as a bellboy and waiter in 1942 and he continued to serve until his death on 18th November 2014. In 1959, he had been working as doorman for several years and was already gaining notoriety as a local celebrity who ran the lobby and reception area of the hotel with military efficiency and courtesy.

Kottarapattu would eventually work as doorman until the grand old age of ninety-four and would become the face of the hotel, with a shock of grey hair and a handlebar moustache, and was famous for his friendly disposition and ability to speak to both king and bellboy alike with the same respect. KC, as he was known, was thirty-nine years old when Ginger, Rocky and Jock first encountered him.

"Good afternoon, gentlemen, and welcome to the Galle Face Hotel, home of the best food, drink and entertainment that Colombo has to offer you. The hotel has three restaurants, three bars and, would you believe it, gentlemen, a public house, or as you may like to call it, 'a pub'.

"The restaurants are suitably named for the establishment: the King of the Mambo, a Cuban restaurant called Firebeach and a less formal, buffet-style offering called the Veranda, where you may indulge in afternoon tea on the terrace should the mood take you. Looking at the splendour of your uniforms, methinks afternoon tea is not for you, oh no."

The three likely lads were mesmerised. KC was working his charm like a cobra with its potential prey.

KC continued his soliloquy.

"The three bars have far more simple names: the Travellers' Bar, the Pool Bar, and the Chequerboard. The third is so named because of the black and white coloured tiles that adorn the floor.

"But unless I am mistaken, gentlemen, you three would be most comfortable in the In… on the Green, our very own version of the quintessential English pub." Quite a crowd had gathered around KC now as he waved his arms about and spoke eloquently to the three army squaddies, as though they had enough money to buy the hotel. He then leant into Ginger and whispered something in his ear, conspiratorially, like a long-lost friend, before leaning back and grinning all over his face like a man who has put an old suit on and found a crumpled five-pound note in the inside jacket pocket.

The three uniformed men were led through several large reception rooms and halls before being shown into what a Colombian architect thought an English pub should look like. There was a lot of wood and, in fact, Jock said, "There's a lot of wood." Small round wooden tables, with wooden stools covered in fake red velvet cushions, were scattered haphazardly around the small drinking area. Tall wooden stools lined the long wooden bar and the alcoves had Tudor-style wooden inserts with high backs and more fake red velvet. There were a couple of strategically placed large wooden beer barrels, and the ceiling was lined with dark wooden beams. Only the light-coloured tiled floor gave away the true location of a hot country as opposed to a country village public house. There were two other people in the bar. It wasn't yet 11am.

Ginger agreed with Jock. "Yeah, you're right. There is a lot of wood." The server behind the bar was dressed in traditional hotel waiter garb. Dark trousers, white ruffled shirt, face like a slapped arse!

"Can I help you with anything, gentlemen?"

Rocky said, "They're all proper mannered around here, aren't they? We will have three pints of whatever you call the bitter around here and we'll all pay for our own." Rocky was a little concerned that one round bought in here might use up every rupee of his shore leave funds.

"Cheapskate," said Ginger.

"Not cheap, just don't know how much this'll cost." As it happened, they didn't have to worry. Conversion from pound sterling to rupee was in their favour, and a pint, even in one of the most famous hotels in the world, was not that much more than a normal pint back home.

"Well, it's beer but not quite what we're used to, but cheers anyway, lads." Ginger toasted his colleagues.

"It's not twelve o'clock yet, but somewhere in the world it is," replied Jock. Rocky just drank and took a good half of his pint in one go.

"Bloody hell, I was ready for that," said Rocky. "Tastes a lot better than it looks."

"Whereas you smell a lot worse than you look."

"Ginger, that doesn't even work. You should leave the

jokes to me and Jock, and you just stick to scaring the locals."

Ginger thought long and hard before hitting on his favourite witticism.

"Piss off, Rocky."

Ginger set the drinking rules.

"Right, now we know the prices, we all buy one more round each in here. That'll get us to a nice starting point of four pints. Then we're off to find some nightlife."

"But it's the middle of the day," Jock shot back.

"It doesn't have to be the middle of the night for the nightlife I'm looking for, Jock." The man who went to Edinburgh on a daytrip once and would forever now be associated with everything Scottish looked puzzled. Ginger spelt it out for him.

"Women, you barm cake."

"Oh, women. What do you want women for? You've a lovely missus and kids at home,"

Rocky joined in. "I don't want anything to do with women. I've only been married nine weeks and most of them have been spent with you two. Lizzie would kill me. And I mean kill me. Probably hammer in the kitchen."

"Well, I do," continued Ginger. "I'm missing home comforts too much and according to Tosh over there behind the bar, we need to head to the Castle Hotel. It's a bit of a dive but will supply the kind of services I'm looking for."

"You dirty dog," said Jock. Ginger just stared at Jock. "Well, not that dirty, obviously." He tried to rescue the situation. Forty minutes later, four pints of cheap frothy lager swilling around their empty innards, the lads set off for the Castle Hotel.

"How far is this place, Ginger? I could do with something to eat, or I won't get to three o'clock." Rocky was feeling the effects of the beer on his empty stomach.

"It's only ten minutes according to Tosh, and you can get something to eat there. Just don't expect home cooking and you should be all right. We follow Galle Face Drive around the bend to the bridge over the river. Then it's a left onto Jamiah Road. Can't miss it apparently. Popular place. There'll be a gang of our lads drinking on the street according to Tosh."

They of course got slightly lost taking a left too early on Galle Face Drive but after a left, right, left – as according to Ginger that's what you always do when lost in a strange city on the other side of the world – they heard the cheers of a gang of army lads sampling the local produce. They soon found the façade of the Castle Hotel. "This looks like the dog's bollocks to me," said Ginger, who was the ship's authority on dog's bollocks. "Come on, let's get in there."

The Castle Hotel had been trading since 1875 but the building was older than that; it's just that no one was absolutely certain how old. It was the finest of dodgy bars, housed in a beautifully ageing neighbourhood on Castle Street, near the Slave Island railway station. The windows had coloured glass tiles, and everything was a beautiful Matrix green or fading orange. Drinks, also, were cheap, and the bites, as no one in their right mind would call them meals, were classed as excellent by local clientele. Rumour also had it that if you could buy it, you could buy it at the Castle Hotel. Plus, rooms could be let by the hour if so required.

"I've heard the meals are great here," said Ginger, and, as reported, no one in their right mind would call them meals.

Rocky asked, "Who exactly told you that, Ginger? We've been with you every step of the way and I don't remember any food critics tipping you off. Oh, I know, let me guess. Tosh, the font of all knowledge."

"Shut up, Rocky. We've got to be back on the ship at 18:00 hours, which gives us four and a bit hours to enjoy ourselves, so you bitch and whine about it or you can get pissed with me and Jock. Your choice!"

"Three pints please then, landlord," laughed Rocky, soon joined by Ginger and Jock. Ginger ordered a platter of the local street food for them all to pick at which included Ceylon zingers, which were strips of chicken cooked in seasoned batter and curry leaves; hotly seasoned burgers; jackfruit burgers, which didn't go down too well; *kottu* wraps, more chicken cooked in garlic, something not used in the kitchens of the north-west of England; finally a plate of cooked cauliflowers and potatoes, highly spiced and covered with melted cheese and grilled chillis. You really didn't want latrine duty after shore leave in Colombo!

The food went down well, and the beer continued to flow. Ginger was finding himself becoming braver and braver in direct proportion to the amount of cheap beer he quaffed. He winked at his mates, now held up by a corner of the room and the table full of empties in front of them. Rocky was done and so was Jock, but he hadn't come to that conclusion yet. Ginger headed off to the bar one last time. It was time for his final purchase of the night. The room was very loud now and full of English accents from many ships, not just the

Empire Fowey. Someone was playing a guitar and the room smelt of too many British troops left out in the sun for far too long, coupled with spilled malt.

Ginger came back with a grin from ear to ear.

"Come on, you two. We have a mission." Jock smiled like Stan Laurel after finding his horn in the short film *Towed in a Hole*, when the whole fishing boat was destroyed. He may not have thought he was 'gone', but he was further down the yellow brick road than Dorothy ever reached. Rocky went along with it for now but was not enamoured. They didn't have long before they were due back on the ship, and he did not fancy trying to carry Ginger back should the need arise.

They exited the front of the hotel and took a left and a left again, leading them around the back. There were four locals playing cards on a small plastic table, each with a clear bottle of an off-yellow liquid. Rocky thought he didn't want to know or ever try tasting what was in the bottles. Ginger asked, "Is one of you lot called Fernando?" They all laughed.

"What's so bloody funny?" asked Ginger. The local men would do well to not cross the large, half-drunk, red-headed Mancunian.

A clean-cut and smartly dressed thin man stood up. He took a lengthy pull from his bottle before smiling, a little like a pike before taking one of your fingers, and said, "Half the male population are called Fernando. It's the most popular name in the country. But, for my sins, I too carry that name. How can I help you?" Ginger went redder than his normal bright red complexion.

"Well, I, erm, thought that…" He leant in and whispered something to Fernando.

All Fernando replied was, "Follow me." With no other plan to refer to, the three compatriots followed Fernando through a maze of side streets. Coming to a junction of five of these side streets, they stopped at a bar. They all knew it was a bar because it was called BAR, and that was it. The owner had decided to keep his marketing policy simple and to the point.

Once inside the dark interior, they realised they were the only English Army men in there, but it was friendly enough and the locals paid them little attention, apart from the man behind the bar who asked them what they were drinking. He also looked a lot like Fernando. Rocky, sobering up a little because he felt that someone had to, just took an orange juice. Ginger and Jock gave him plenty of grief, but he didn't mind. Fernando also took a beer, but a bottle, not the 'stuff' the 'tourists' got sold. Fernando spoke.

"Okay, Mr Ginger. In a moment, you go up the stairs to meet my sister. She is very beautiful girl but no rough stuff. Be nice to her, she be nice to you. I be outside, listening. You buy one more beer, Mr Ginger, but for this much." Fernando showed Ginger a grotty piece of paper folded so many times that it was almost through on the creases.

"For a beer?" shouted Ginger.

"I can sell beer for any price, Mr Ginger, but I cannot sell my sister, if you be so kind to understand." Ginger took a bundle of rupees from his pocket and handed them across to Fernando.

"No, Mr Ginger, the barman will take your money and give you another beer."

"Oh yeah. Of course," muttered Ginger. The expensive

beer transaction took place and then Fernando asked Ginger to follow him again.

"What do we do?" asked Jock.

"Not my problem," smirked Ginger, "but you may wish to stand outside after your drinks. These lads may not be as hospitable without the Big Ginge to look after you." These were his last words of encouragement before he followed Fernando through a set of hanging beads and up a tight metal staircase, so tight that Ginger's shoulders touched the wall on one side and hung over the handrail on the other.

A small landing with no light, artificial or otherwise, awaited them at the top. Fernando gave his last talk to Ginger.

"My sister's name is Tharindu, which in your language means 'Moon'. A beautiful name for a beautiful girl. I will see you into this room now, where you will remove your clothes. I will stay in that room, and you will go through to the bedroom where Tharindu awaits you. I will lock the door until you are finished, and no one will disturb you. Is this understood, Mr Ginger?"

"I guess so but I'm not taking my pants off in front of you?"

Fernando merely shook his head and walked through the first door. Ginger followed and was stood in a tiny room with nothing but a chair and a bare bulb hanging down on its wire.

"Place your shirt and shorts on the chair, Mr Ginger. You can leave your pants on if you so wish."

"Why do I have to do that?"

"You don't have to. We can go back downstairs, and you will never meet my sister Tharindu." The short, dark-haired, dark-skinned man, with a whispery moustache, tapped his foot with impatience.

"Beautiful, you say?"

"Like a full moon on a cloudless night, Mr Ginger."

"All right then, but no funny business."

"No funny business, just business," retorted Fernando.

Ginger whipped off his shirt and put it over the back of the chair. He removed his boots and pulled his shorts down, glancing over his shoulder at Fernando as he did so. Fernando stepped forward and, pulling a large brass key from his pocket, unlocked the door. The lock clicked like a gunshot and Ginger flinched. Fernando left the door closed and stood back, raising his arm like a waiter showing a guest to his chair.

"Tharindu awaits you, Mr Ginger."

Ginger pushed the handle down and strolled into the room. The light was extremely bright, and he held his hand over his eyes. Somebody, he assumed Fernando, pushed him hard in the small of his back. Putting his hands out and away from his eyes, Ginger hit upon something metal that he grabbed.

Bedstead, thought Ginger, whose eyes were still screwed up. He heard the door slam behind him and heard the gunshot lock crack again as the door was quickly slammed shut and the key turned. It was then that Ginger became aware of the gentle warm breeze blowing into his face followed by the realisation as he finally opened his eyes wide enough that the bedstead he firmly gripped in his bear-sized hands was a balcony rail.

"Oh shit."

He was looking into a side street of which he had no discernible memory. He wasn't sure if it was a street he had walked when following Fernando to get there or not. He thought he was at the rear of the BAR if his internal compass hadn't let him down, but after everything he'd drank in the past few hours, he couldn't be sure.

What he did know was that he was stood in his white baggy army-issue underpants and socks, locked on a tiny balcony somewhere in Colombo. He thanked every god that had ever been thought of for the fact he had slipped his wallet into his sock before stepping 'into the light', through the dressing-room door.

"Shit, bastard, fuck." The holy trinity of swearing erupted from him as he bellowed them into the warm Colombo afternoon air. He turned, banging on the door and kicking it until his foot started to bleed. This wasn't the first time this had happened, and the door was sturdy enough to do its job, which was to keep burly army recruits on the other side until Fernando could make his escape.

Ginger turned back and looked over the balcony. *Twenty, perhaps twenty-five feet*, he thought, *I can drop that.* He climbed over the edge but within seconds was back on the safer side. He couldn't make that drop without doing some considerable damage. He bellowed again like a bull in heat, which effectively ten minutes earlier was exactly what he had been.

Meanwhile, back downstairs, Rocky watched as Fernando came quickly back through the beaded curtain carrying a bag. The dark man walked to the bar, exchanged a few short, sharp words with the barman when money changed hands and then left by the front door of the bar, either not seeing Rocky and Jock or totally ignoring them. Jock had one eye up the chimney and the other down the pot and didn't even notice Fernando had returned.

Rocky said to Jock, "I'm sure I overheard him saying to Ginger he would wait for him. He wouldn't walk out the bar and leave his sister with a squaddie he's only just met. Especially not one who looks like Ginger looks." Rocky waited five minutes and then took the situation into his own hands and, ignoring the barman's shouts, went through the beaded curtain from whence Fernando had just returned. His common sense took him up the stairs to the landing. From there, he needed no more of his common sense, so-called because it is far from common, as he heard the bellows of his mate through two doors.

He tried each of the doors in turn before finding the one where Ginger's shouts were coming from. From there, he saw the door ahead of him, bending on its hinges.

"Ginger," he shouted. And then again as Ginger's screams were stopping him from hearing Rocky. "GINGER," and this time Rocky banged on the door himself. Ginger stopped shouting.

"Rocky," he said in as close to a normal voice as he could muster.

"Ginger, it's Rocky."

"I know it's fucking Rocky. Get me out, you dickhead."

"Dickhead. You're the one trapped in a cupboard, Ginger."

"It's not a cupboard, it's..." Poor Ginger sounded totally exasperated.

"Okay, please, just get me out," pleaded the big man.

"Wait there. I'll speak to the barman."

Rocky danced down the stairs three at a time, grabbed a startled Jock and went to the bar. The original barman had unsurprisingly gone and there was an elderly lady now pouring the drinks. Rocky tried to explain but either the bar lady had no English or, as Rocky suspected, chose to have no English. He was getting nowhere; Jock was no use whatsoever and the clientele were looking at him in a very unfriendly manner as he raised his voice. Using the typical Englishman abroad way of being understood in a different language, he shouted English instead of speaking it.

Rocky tried a different tactic. He spoke slower and gently, and the lady leant forward slightly to hear what he had to say. Rocky said, "I now know you understand me because you got closer to hear me. My friend upstairs is a very large man who could cause a lot of trouble. He will smash your door to pieces in a second and you will have to pay for the repairs. If you have a key, and I think you know which room I need the key for, give it to me and the door will stay in one piece."

The woman shrugged her shoulders, dipped her hand into a pocket of her dress that Rocky didn't even know existed and threw a heavy brass key onto the bar.

Rocky snatched it up.

"Thank you. I don't know how good your English is, but that decision makes great sense. C'mon, Jock, let's go and get Ginger." Back up the stairs again, Ginger was shouting again and banging on the door and seconds later the three mates were stood facing each other in the dressing room.

"Where's my shirt and shorts?" asked Ginger.

"I guess Fernando has them," said Jock. Even staggering drunk Jock could work out the scam.

"Come on," said Ginger, "I'm getting my money back. And my clothes!" Back down the stairs, now wobbling with the size of Ginger running and Rocky and Jock not far behind him. Through the beaded curtain and into a reception party. The men previously drinking had all gathered together around the bar, eight of them, and the lady of the household had a machete in her hand.

Ginger knew no fear and he quickly jumped the bar and grabbed a knife that had previously been used for cutting fruit. This was rapidly getting out of hand. The machete was transferred to the biggest of the men and after jumping back over the bar, the three Englishmen faced off against the Ceylonese. The knife that Ginger picked up wouldn't have cut his nails; the knife wielded by the mob could have cut a palm tree in half.

Rocky was holding Jock on his feet. He would have to drop him to fight. This really wasn't worth it.

"Ginger, leave it. If it were just a fistfight then fine, but someone could get seriously hurt. We can always come back with the lads on ship. Use some sense, man." Ginger nodded and the three men backed slowly from the room.

"They can keep the money," said Ginger, "but I'm not running away." They reversed into the sunlight and then Ginger pushed Rocky and Jock behind him.

"Turn and walk slowly. Do not run. Run and they'll chase us. And then I'll turn and fight, and I hope you two will too." Rocky did as he was asked. Ginger stood still, snarling obscenities, retaining as much dignity as possible when holding off an angry mob in his army jockey shorts. He then turned and walked after Rocky and Jock. They turned the first corner and then ran as fast as they could, with Jock hanging miserably between them like a drunken hooker.

"Did we win?" he slurred.

"Shut it, Jock," said Rocky, "or Ginger might just drop you and steal your shorts." Then Rocky spurted a laugh out that he'd been trying to hold in. Jock just roared and then a moment later Ginger joined in.

Laughing between words, he said, "It's okay for you two. I've got to tell the sarge that I've left me shorts in a Colombo brothel." They were still laughing when they got back to the ship, but not for long.

St Helens, Merseyside

1975

The morning had not gone to plan. I was back home again by half eleven. The flasher, forever now known as Richard Head, had messed up the day's arrangements. We were going to the fields in the afternoon for football or cricket, no one had yet specified; it tended to be decided by whoever called for whomever first and what sporting kit they had decided on. It was Charlie and Mush who had a cricket bat and wickets, so they tended to call the shots on a game of cricket. But I'd been banished for laughing too much.

Anyway, the morning had not gone to plan. We should all still have been swinging over the stream in the woods now. The Dobey twins didn't like cricket so if they started the round of calls – *Can Graham come out to play?* – it was for a game of football. I don't remember us ever calling it soccer then, just football or footy. The point I'm trying to make is, this was a woods morning and it had all gone belly up. I think I'd told Dad if I wasn't home for lunch, then don't worry as it was a woods and fields day, but now here I was at home. Bored. Not desperately tear-the-house-down bored, but bored enough to get myself into bother if I wasn't careful.

If there had been an Olympic sport for getting into bother through mischief, I would have been on the medal rostrum every four years, and I'd have won medals at the Europeans, Commonwealth and World games as well. I wasn't wilfully naughty; I just pushed the envelope until it became a pillowcase and then I still ripped it. It wasn't malicious, just inquisitive and, even if I say so myself, creative.

For example, in our north-west '70s household we had a shield with crossed swords hanging over the mantelpiece. It wasn't a staple in houses in those days but there was a '70s period when medieval military was reintroduced into the décor of a living room.

On one occasion, Charlie, Mush, my younger brother, David, and I were in ours on a rainy day. The morning television for children lasted for about forty-five minutes in those days and included such things as *Why Don't You Just Switch Off Your Television Set and Go Out and Do Something Less Boring Instead?* Really, that's what it was called. So, we did. And the more interesting thing we did was play 'Knights in shining armour'. We were definitely too old to be playing this foolish game, especially with glass sliding doors separating the front room from the back in our three-bedroom semi, but we'd never played it with real live swords from the olden days!

Now, I have to be fair here and say that the others were not as keen as I was to take the swords down from above the fire. For a start, Charlie and Mush were in someone else's house and they were the kind of lads that wouldn't have dreamt of behaving in that way, and our David was four years younger than me. What I'm trying to say is that in a court of law I'm the one who would be held responsible, while the other three would get off with a slap on the wrists.

I got the swords down, which was a task in itself as they were tucked behind the shield in a crossed swords position, but they could be drawn upwards and out from behind the shield casing. At this point, I did think, *I'm never getting these back in place*, but it was too late for that and anyway it was still pouring it down outside. We weren't daft, though, so we moved all the furniture to the edge of the room and opened the sliding doors to their fullest, thus giving us the biggest space possible across the two-room area.

I think we saw ourselves more as the sands-and-sandals-type warriors, Spartacus or in fantasy, Jason and the Argonauts. These captured our imagination more than the straightforward Arthurian legend. Plus, I had started reading the *Lord of the Rings* trilogy by then so saw myself as something of a Strider before he became Aragorn. We all agreed he was cooler as Strider. I gave Charlie a sword and he was reluctant but only until I tried to hit him with my sword and then he started to defend himself. As stupid as all this sounds, we were relatively sensible. No one tried to run anyone through; we were more interested in bashing the swords together and in all honesty the knives used to butter your bread were sharper. We took it in turns battling away for about thirty minutes until we knew we had ridden our luck as far as she was prepared to canter that day, and decided to finish and put the swords back on the wall. Then we would get the furniture back in position before an adult turned up and decided to use one of the swords on us.

I don't know what movie or TV show I had seen my next move in, it had a feel of Zorro about it, but with a flourish I put my sword back into its make-believe sheath, one that pointed backwards and away from your hip. (I now know this to be called a tail guard.) It was my final move and I said something along the lines of, "Thank you for the sport, gentlemen, but you'll never be able to kill the great Strider," or something equally as flamboyant.

Unfortunately for me, someone had closed the glass sliding doors as we started to put the furniture back and the sword went straight through one of the glass panels, sending broken glass everywhere and we were all just wearing our socks, shoes left by the back door on a rainy day. I couldn't believe it. We had managed thirty sword fights and battles and not touched a thing in the house and with my last touch of swordsmanship I had broken the bloody window in the sliding doors. It really was sooooo unfair.

On another particularly inventive day at school (I went to an all-boys grammar school called Eastfield, one of the last grammar schools governed by the De La Salle brothers), I got myself into terrible trouble again. The travelling fair had set up camp on our local playing fields, the ones where we played all our football and cricket, and after spending all my money on the only two rides worth going on, the Waltzer and the dodgem cars, I had managed to win a goldfish by throwing a table tennis ball into a fish bowl, the sort that they always had fish in on *Tom and Jerry*.

I carried the fish home in the regulation plastic bag and put it in a jelly-making bowl until Mum had the opportunity to buy me a proper bowl from the pet shop and a bag of feed that would last Moby (great name), if I fed him once a day as suggested by Dad, until he was twenty-two years old. He lasted three days and then I think died of overfeeding. I have no idea why, but I put him in a matchbox and popped him into my blazer pocket to take to school.

Taking a dead goldfish to school in a matchbox seemed like a promising idea to a thirteen-year-old schoolboy. So, after the obligatory 'show and tell' to all my mates, I still didn't know what form of dignified send-off I wanted to give to good old Moby, who had brought me seconds of pleasure over the three days. Double Maths saved the day and solved my problem. Our maths teacher was a previous pupil of the school who had been off to university for three years before coming back as a raring-to-go twenty-one-year-old enthusiastic, principled old boy who wanted to change the world and become Mr Chips. Or, as we liked to call him, fresh meat.

Mr Cummings was the nicest young bloke on the planet but put him in front of a class of rowdy, cheeky school lads and he struggled. Did we take advantage of him? Yes, we did. Did we cheek him every chance we got? Yes, we did. Did we prank him when we could? Yes, I did. I decided that the only proper way to give Moby the send-off he so deserved was to pin him to the blackboard for Mr Cummings's lesson.

The school was old school, and the blackboards were three rotating boards on a long drum so that the majority of one was always visible to the class. In between the three boards was a metal strip that joined them together, but which could also hold a small package, like a matchbox, for example. The first thing that Cummings always did when he came into the room was quickly clean each of the three boards, boisterously pulling the board downwards to the next so that he could start with three clean boards. Literally the definition of starting with a clean slate.

On this particular day, the plan worked perfectly. He bent down to rotate the board from the bottom, pulling hard as he always did, thus spilling the open matchbox from the uppermost metal strip and dropping a dead fish called Moby straight onto his head. He jumped. He knew something had hit him but what, he didn't know. We all jumped, thirty-three of us, because he had jumped, emitting a little squeak at the same time. He bent to see what was on the floor, poking the matchbox with the toe of his shoe, at which point Moby slipped off his head and onto the floor. This time, he gave a little scream.

A lot of the lads screamed as well because only the inner circle was in on the joke. Everyone was shouting and laughing plus banging the lids of our desks, a very grammar school thing to do. Meanwhile, Cummings was poking a dead fish and a matchbox around the front of the classroom. When he realised what it was, it's fair to say he wasn't happy. He had never got angry but that was the final day I could use that statement.

"WHO DID THIS?" Absolute silence. When a man who never gets angry gets angry, it has a profound effect, especially if he's a teacher of a class of teenage lads.

"I'LL ASK ONE MORE TIME AND IF I DON'T GET AN ANSWER, EVERY ONE OF YOU IS BACK HERE ON SATURDAY."

My inner sanctum had in the space of a few seconds become a stranger to me. Quite a few mates stared directly at me as if to say, *Come on, Locky, do the right thing.* (Locky as in Sherlock Holmes as opposed to Graham Holmes.) I wasn't exactly given up as public enemy number 1 but my hundreds of best mates were disappearing over the horizon. Cummings looked directly at me, which wasn't easy as I was in the back row.

"Holmes, stand up." I did.

"Did you do this?" Barely a whisper.

"Yessir." The words rolled into one. My eyes downcast. I knew I was in trouble and surprisingly I did feel guilty. He was the nicest teacher in the world, and he liked me because I loved Maths, and I had humiliated him for a cheap laugh. I didn't have those complex feelings then as a child, they came later, but I do remember the feelings of regret at upsetting this bloke who wasn't that much older than we all were.

"Get out. Headmaster's office, now."

"Yessir."

"And pick your rubbish up on the way out."

"Yessir." I still couldn't help myself, though, and when I picked Moby up, I wiggled him in some front-row Charlie's face as though he was still alive. Everyone laughed again and I could hear Cummings once more shouting at me as I shut the classroom door quickly behind me. I got tanned for that one. Head wasn't in so I was unlucky enough to get the deputy head, whose favourite pastime, apart from drinking the communion wine, was beating small boys with a leather strap. Two on each hand that day.

But it was worth it!

The point I'm trying to make is, I was naughty but not nasty naughty. I was basically the fool. And I didn't need to act. If I could get a laugh or a *I can't believe you did that*, then that would make my day.

Back to the day in question and wondering what to do next after Richard Head had messed the day up. I would play SPOT on my own in the back, but the back was grass so I needed some boots. You couldn't really play SPOT on your own, but I was pretty good at making some solitaire rules up with a ball and a wall to kick it against. I decided I needed my boots, which I knew were somewhere in the black hole we called 'Under t'stairs'.

Girding my loins for an expedition for which I wrote and left my last will and testament (I pinned it to the fridge, leaving everything to Charlie including all my old St Helens rugby league programmes), I opened the wooden door that led into a living hell.

Under t'stairs had previously been just a space, a part of the house that was virtually never used or that 'stuff' just used to get dumped in, such as dirty shoes when we came in from the outside. Dad said it was under-utilised, which was a word he had started to use a lot since he became shop steward for his union at work. His ploy to tackle this problem was to board it up and put a door on it, thus creating the black hole. There was no light in there and the door was in the middle of the wooden panels.

Items that were used regularly were placed near the door so the light from the hall at least gave you a fighting chance of looking for whatever it was that had led you to this point. So, the vacuum cleaner was there, within the light, or as we called it, 'the Hoover'. Any sports bags that were used on a regular basis stayed in the light. Shoes, boots, or wellies that were also regular attire, regular not having a definition and very much in the eye of the beholder. As you ventured through the door, akin to the moment in a horror film when the female lead chooses to wander off in the dark and her torch fails on her, items took on a more incomprehensible view.

The old coat hangers were on the highest point of the wall, and there were coats up there that hadn't been used since the 1950s, and the house was only built in 1965. These sat along the wall like dark sentinels guarding the contents of the tomb.

Old coffee tables, old lamps; discarded items of clothing; sports bags; sports kit; football boots, rugby boots, fashion boots, any old boots; a shoe rack that fell forward onto you if you looked at it askance; Christmas decorations but only the stand-by ones (who has stand-by Christmas decorations?); a discarded briefcase; pictures that had been taken down but were too good to be thrown away so would be kept in the dark under the stairs for the rest of their existence instead, where nobody could see them; a folded-up metal clothes horse that wrestled with you every time you ventured in; tools, too many to bore us all with; and finally boxes, lots and lots of boxes.

Many of the boxes had originally been used for footwear and as my desired goal was to find a pair of boots, I concentrated on the smaller shoe boxes. Any would do as all three of us wore them, yes, even my sister, Anne, and with us all growing rapidly there would be at least half a dozen pairs under there. Mum and Dad never had to worry about what to buy us for Christmas or birthdays as we would always need new boots.

Holding a torch in my mouth with a flickering light, I tried to find something I could use. It wasn't even a proper torch but one of those stocking filler torches that by rotating a little switch with some coloured filters would produce different coloured beams of light. As I was holding this in my mouth and catching the little switch with my tongue, it was like looking for something on the floor of the school disco. Red, yellow, green; I didn't know whether to find the boots or do some *Jive Talkin'* with the Bee Gees.

After scuttling around on the floor like a hermit crab for ten or more minutes, I pulled out several boxes into the now-dazzling light of the hall. Sat cross-legged, I started to go through the contents. There was lots of old paperwork, receipts for purchases, Kays catalogue payment books and the rest were mostly empty. No boots. I came to the last one and it was packed with documents that due to the embossed headers and coloured seals looked more important than the rest.

I was still sitting there twenty minutes later when my dad came through the back door clutching his bag of Pimbletts pies. He clocked me on the floor of the hallway, covered in dust with open boxes all around me, and that was when I asked him the question that had kept my head spinning for the full twenty minutes:

"Am I adopted, Dad?"

Hampton, London

1978

It was a cold funeral but there's an argument that says every funeral is cold, and so they should be. Cold as in a bitter wind that cuts through every layer of clothes you have on and still manages to reach your bones. There were less than fifteen people in the church, and that included a member of the clergy and two altar boys. Bert and Mary Church and their daughter, Jayne, were the main mourners, along with Rita from the corner shop, Davide the Italian fish and chip shop man and several professional mourners who went to every funeral. *My highlight of the week*, one said to the other. The wind sighed outside as if wishing to join in the ceremony.

That's what a funeral is; it is a ceremony. A celebration of life by modern parlance. There was little celebration in St Mary's church, Hampton, on a miserable freezing day in January 1978. The vicar, Alan Cumberland, had never met Uncle Ted; Bert and Mary were not for standing and saying a few words at any social gathering and so a few platitudes were mumbled by the vicar about Ted's war record and that was that. The coffin was wheeled out by Spencer and Sons, put in the hearse and away to Hampton Cemetery, which was located in the cheerily named Hollybush Lane, surely a place in one of Enid Blyton's *Famous Five* children's novels?

The wind whipped an icy sheet of sleet across the three mourners who braved the arctic conditions, and the vicar's vestments whipped around him like a bird of paradise trying to take off. Take off in a blizzard. The three were, of course, Bert, Mary and Jayne, who had taken a day off from sixth form college where she was studying Economics, Business Studies and Mathematics. The vicar speed read the service, finishing with the Resurrection Prayer.

'I am the resurrection and the Life,
Saith the Lord: He that believeth in me, though he were dead, yet shall he live:
and whosoever liveth and believeth in me, shall never die.
I know that my redeemer liveth, and that he shall stand at the latter day upon the earth:
and though his body be destroyed, yet shall I see God: whom I shall see for myself,
and mine eyes shall behold, and not as a stranger.
We brought nothing into this world, and it is certain we can carry nothing out.
The Lord gave, and the Lord hath taken away; blessed be the name of the Lord.

Amen'

"Amen," responded the three wet and bedraggled mourners. The vicar thanked them and then without further pomp left in a hurry, followed by two surly and disgruntled altar boys. They flapped back in such a hurry across the graveyard, like three hens struggling to get back to the henhouse in a sudden storm.

Bert spoke first.

"Time for a pint. Let's get ourselves back and we'll go in the Station and raise a toast to poor old Ted." The Station was their local, a few hundred yards from where they lived in Old Road and unsurprisingly a few hundred yards away from the railway station. In fact, the platform nearly reached the back garden of the public house before veering left and heading off towards London Waterloo. The bottles on the shelves of the Station pub would rattle when a train not stopping at Hampton sped through.

After a short but difficult walk into the sleet coming in from the east, they arrived at the Station public house. The pub had been sat in the dip by the edge of the platform for over one hundred years, and looked as though it had. It was a real old-fashioned pub with a public bar and a snug; heavy dark wood furniture surrounded the bar, and the lighting inside was marginally better than the overcast skies they left behind them as they passed through the double entrance. A door from the front yard, a tiny lobby and then a choice of two doors, one into the snug and the other into the bar. The only difference on the inside was that one was smaller than the other and the public bar was mostly frequented by any men who entered the pub on their own. Probably eighty per cent of the clientele.

Into the snug passed the Churches.

"Pint of Best, a ginger wine and a Babycham, please, Mick," ordered Bert. On the day of a funeral, Jayne would be treated as an adult and although ten months from being legal, no one seemed to bother over a Babycham. The ladies had plonked themselves down with their backs against the cushion of a little alcove that just allowed them to squash in next to each other. Bert brought the drinks over and sat opposite them on a stool.

"Cheers, Ted, hope you've gone somewhere nice," said Bert, raising his glass.

The others clinked theirs against his and then Mary said, "Are you not going to say something better than that, Bert? It's not much of a send-off."

"Ted wasn't much for fuss," replied Bert. "He wouldn't want a big speech or anything like that."

Mary looked at her daughter, Jayne, as if asking her if she fancied saying a few words, all communicated from mother to daughter in the raising of an eyebrow.

"Don't look at me, Mum, I knew Uncle Ted as a kid but for the past two years I've hardly spoken to him apart from in passing."

"He loved you like one of his own, he did," said Mary. "Would have done anything for you. Never missed a birthday, got you a selection box every Christmas, even built you a snowman one year, I remember."

"I do remember, and I was and still am grateful for his friendship, but you don't make a speech at somebody's funeral because they once built you a snowman."

"To be fair, he got the proportions so wrong it looked like

Quasimodo," laughed Bert. "And he didn't have a carrot for its nose so put a small beetroot there instead. We had the only alcoholic snowman in Middlesex with its bulbous red nose." They all laughed genuinely. It was a fond memory of a man of whom they had all in their own way been genuinely fond.

"Don't know what we'll do on Christmas morning this year," said Mary, "We always went into Ted's for a sherry."

Bert answered.

"Don't worry. We can always have a drink with Ted at ours at Christmas. We can leave two glasses of sherry underneath the stockings, one for Father Christmas and one for Ted." Jayne felt a cold shudder run through her. She wasn't too sure about the fun in leaving drinks out for dead men, Uncle Ted or otherwise.

"That sounds creepy, Dad. I think I would rather we just toasted him." Mary looked at Bert, Bert looked at Jayne and then back at his wife.

"What?" asked Jayne. "I can see the way you two are looking at each other. Tell me, what's going on?"

"Nothing is going on," answered Mary. "I have something for you and now seems as good a time as any to give it to you. Because you've been busy with college and all that since Uncle Ted took really bad, he's written you a letter." Mary handed over a plain brown envelope with the word Jayne neatly scrawled across the front. Jayne took the envelope from her mother and placed it on the table in front of her, carefully avoiding the spillage from her dad's pint of Best.

"Well, aren't you going to open it then?" Bert asked.

"I prefer to do it later when I'm on my own," answered

his daughter. "I don't want to open it sat in the pub, it's disrespectful."

"Ted won't be bothered. I'm just nosy as to what he wanted to say to you. He could hardly lift a pen at the end but about a fortnight ago asked your mum to get him a pen and paper. Said he needed to leave you a message before he went. Made it sound like he was going for a paper, not going for good." Bert stopped and took a large swig of the now-flat brown liquid in front of him, before making a quick decision and downing the lot. "Time for another," he smiled. "Ladies?"

Both Mary and Jayne answered with a shake of their heads.

"Cheap round," said Bert. Rising, he went back over to the bar, leaving his wife and daughter in silence sat at the table. Jayne finished her Babycham, picked the brown envelope up from amid the spillage and placed it in her black bag, borrowed from her mum for the occasion.

Mary finished her drink also and when Bert came back told him, "We're going to leave you to it, Bert. Take your time."

"Last orders is three o'clock anyway, love. I won't be long. A couple of the blokes from bowls are in the other side so I'll just pop my head in."

The greying, slightly overweight middle-aged lady pulled herself to her feet and pecked Bert on the cheek, tears in her eyes. She had become uncomfortable sat in the pub in her funeral black, and the emotion of the day was telling on her. She needed some quiet time and perhaps a little lie-down, something she rarely did. She was surprised at the strength of feeling that had washed over her, starting when she had passed Jayne the letter. The thought of Ted, in his agonies, making the effort to leave a goodbye note for Jayne had touched her more than she normally allowed.

"Come on. Mum. I'll come with you. Get the kettle on. Perhaps put a drop of brandy in your tea if there's any left from Christmas." Jayne held her mum by the elbow and led her out of the Station public house.

Once home, 41 Old Road, Jayne was as good as her word, and they were both soon sat at the kitchen table drinking Typhoo tea, Mary's laced liberally with Martell brandy. They mostly talked about Jayne's college in Twickenham and how Jayne had adapted to life there rather than at school. Plus, by working in retail on Saturdays in Kingston, how she was staying economically on the right side of the breadline. She had also found herself a job waiting on in a local hotel three times a week, and that helped her to run the little second-hand Hillman Imp that her parents had funded; funded in the hope that once Jayne took herself off to university, it would encourage her to make regular trips home. So far, Jayne had managed to balance her parents' wishes and her own social life so that all were happy.

She excused herself and went to her room to change into something a little less drab. Unpacking the handbag borrowed from her mum, she sat on the edge of the single bed. She knew she was in the right room as it still had adorned on the walls posters of Donny Osmond, David Cassidy and, of course, the Bay City Rollers, which were at least five years old, ripped from magazines she had once bought religiously with her pocket money. With a t-shirt and short skirt ensemble, legs hanging over the edge of the bed and posters on the wall, she looked every year of fourteen and not the seventeen plus she was. She ripped open the letter and read.

Hello Jayne,

I hope today has not been too difficult for you. I'm sorry I didn't get the chance to say goodbye to you face to face, which if you're reading this means we didn't. It's been fun while it lasted. As your dad would say, I've had a good innings. I saw some things in the war that people aren't supposed to see, and I'll take them to my grave with me which, without being too morbid, is probably where I am now. He he!

My son is overseas, and I just want to say thank you to you for becoming like a niece to me. Since you were born in 1960, you've been an ever present in my life and you're now a young woman who's a credit to Bert and Mary.

There's a couple of things I'd like you to do for me if that's all right. Just petty things, shouldn't be too much bother, just like the errands you used to run for me when you were younger. I've left some money in the house, not a lot, about £1,000 I reckon. There's a loose tile on the fireplace, you'll find it. Under it is a tin with the money.

Will you ask Tony at the Station to put £50 behind the bar to buy the bowls lads a few drinks until the money runs out?

Will you look after the garden for me with your dad? There's some things he's not going to be able to manage. I've left him the bottom of my garden – well, to him and your mum – in my will so soon it will be his. I'd just like to think my plants and flowers are going to be kept well. Take money if you need it.

Finally, I want you to take the rest of my money and find yourself a nice young man and put a deposit down on a house for yourselves. I was in love once, a long long time ago. Thought I was the best cockerel in the henhouse, I did. I want you to do this because I didn't. I had my chance and I buggered it up, excuse my language. I've regretted it ever since. It's a bit of a secret to be honest. I'll tell you about it one day.

I'm tired now so that's me. Take care, live a good life and look out for me. I'm going to keep in touch, you know.

Cheers, Uncle Ted

Jayne took the letter back down the stairs and handed it to her mum and waited while Mary caught up.

"What do you make of that, Mum?"

Mary answered.

"First things first. Here, take Ted's front door key. Off you go and get that tin from his hearth. Then we can see what the rest means." Jayne did as she was told, just like she had all of her life. Crossing her mother was a pastime that Jayne had realised from an early age usually finished with her winning silver and her mum taking the gold. Running to number 39, she didn't wait about. Key in, turning left immediately into the living room, or the front room in these old two-up two-down cottages.

The house was already cold as her dad had turned all the heating off when Uncle Ted had passed away, and it was January, but Jayne would have lied if she had said she wasn't a little unnerved. *Don't be stupid*, she told herself, *it's only Ted's things and you've seen them a thousand times before.* She walked around the two-seater couch to the fireplace and knelt down. The fire was an open Edwardian one with the debris of a fairly recent coal fire lit by her dad. Around it on the wall and the floor Ted had laid a variety of different-shaped stone tiles, giving it a very 1970s look. Running her hands along the floor tiles, she waited for a wobble or one to rock slightly but none did. *Well, this isn't as easy as Uncle Ted had suggested,* she thought. She had an idea.

Jumping up, she headed into the kitchen, got herself a glass of water (once more, she knew where everything was kept after years of coming in here as a child) and brought it back to the hearth, again kneeling down on the floor. Then Jayne very gently commenced pouring the water over the right-hand side of the tiled hearth, watching how the water flowed, and then she had it. Third tile from the top on the left-hand side, the water drained below it; there was obviously a hollow beneath it.

On the right of the fire was a small ornamental poker and brush set that looked so new that it could have come straight from the wrapper. Taking the poker, Jayne prised it under the tile beneath which the water had vanished and like David Nixon on the television, there was the tin box. It was then that Jayne heard the scraping. She shivered and looked around her and her breath billowed out in the frigid air. The house had been cold when she walked in, but it had now worsened as she had left the front door ajar. This logic escaped her as sure as her icy breath escaped her mouth. Then she heard the scraping again. It was like someone was dragging a table across a floor, a table like the one in the kitchen.

A voice whispered across the living room, "Jayne!"

Jayne screamed and her dad said, "All right, love. It's only me. Your mum sent me in to see how you was getting on." Even though she was seventeen years old, Jayne grabbed her dad and hugged him.

"Don't be silly. You got yourself spooked, is all. It's been a tiring and emotional day. Let's lock up and get a nice cup of tea with your mum."

"But I heard something scraping, Dad."

"It was just the front door in the wind. You left it wide open with the key in. Listen." Bert held the door in his hand and quickly moved it back and forth, emitting a squeal from the troubled hinges.

"Needs a spot of WD-40, that's all you heard." Jayne listened but wasn't convinced. The door squeaking was not what she heard earlier but she let it go. Her dad was happy with the explanation, and she was sure there was a sensible explanation for her noise; she just didn't have it yet. Jayne was quite pragmatic and would work out a solution given enough time, plus she wasn't easily frightened. You didn't go to live in Bristol on your own at eighteen years of age if easily frightened, and that's where Jayne wanted to go to university.

It wasn't long before Bert, Mary and Jayne were once more sat around the kitchen table with steaming hot cups of tea and chocolate biscuits. The tin that Jayne had recovered was sat in the middle between them all.

"Well, aren't you going to open it, Jayne?" asked her dad.

"Read the letter first, Dad, then we will all be at the same point." She waited while Bert did just that. His hand was shaking slightly as he did so, but there was always a smile on his crooked mouth, one that rose slightly more on the left than the right, as he read.

"Good old Ted. Mysterious to the last." Looking at his wife, he asked, "Do you know what this secret is Ted refers to in his letter?"

"No idea. He never told me any secrets of the heart. I know his marriage was a tough one with little love shown, but they all cared for each other. At least I thought they did, but I'll never know why Ted didn't go to Canada with them all. Plus, you'd have thought someone would have come back for their father's funeral. He said he loved in this letter, but I don't know who that is he loved. I don't even know the name of his wife and son in Canada, if that's where they still are. He wouldn't tell me or your dad, Jayne. I think he felt a bit embarrassed about letting them go."

"Do they even know he's dead then?" asked Jayne

Bert took the story reins.

"Solicitor got in touch with them that's still around. According to his will, he wanted me and your mum to arrange his funeral, but we haven't seen the will, just received the request from his solicitor. Funny-looking man, Edward Carter, his name from Able, Brown and Carter. Anyway, back to Ted. He was a good friend to me, and your mum, and I'd like to think we were to him. I never pushed him on stuff he didn't want to tell me and vice versa. We fought in separate wars but neither of us were big on sharing. So, if he didn't want to tell me about his family, that was fine by me."

Jayne took a slurp of tea and a chunk of chocolate biscuit. Outside, it was almost dark and the sleet was still swirling around the streetlamps. She reached for the tin.

"Perhaps this might help?" Inside, she found nine neatly bundled, held in place by elastic bands, tubes of ten-pound notes. There were some loose ten-pound, five-pound and one-pound notes. There was a banker's plastic bag of coins. Underneath them there was a light blue envelope. Inside was an old, faded photograph.

"Who's that?" asked Jayne.

"Not sure, love," answered her mum, "but I think we now know who Ted fell in love with!"

Christleton, Cheshire

2019

Anne started by having to fill in the Hereditary online form, or consultation. She wasn't sure about doing this; Dad had never wanted any of them to pursue the past, if that was even possible. Did you pursue the past or did it pursue you? She had to be in control of this process; do it properly as such. There would be nothing worse for her than becoming a cog in yet another of society's wheels. Hereditary had a good reputation and she read the small print again; she could pull the plug anytime she wanted. The problem was, it was very difficult to put the toothpaste back in the tube once you'd squeezed it.

Question number one: *Full Name.* Well, if she got this wrong, it was time to call it a day. Anne Elizabeth Smith. One out of one; she was doing well.

Question number two: *Email.* This was a little trickier. Damn these question setters leading her into a false sense of security. She smiled to herself. It was many years since she sat an exam but funnily enough, she was experiencing the same butterflies. She went onto Google mail and set up a random new email account specifically for using with Hereditary. She looked around her desk and picked up a book, one that she had only just started but had meant to read all her life: *The Road to Wigan Pier*, by George Orwell. Opening the book randomly, page 88, there was a shopping list. Her new email became: RentClothingClubCoal@gmail.com and the password was GasMilkUnionFees. Let anyone try to hack that!

She was getting the hang of this; she was pretty sure she was two from two. Okay, throw your worst at me, question setter.

Question number three: *Phone*. She dabbled with typing, *Yes, please*, but thought that a little childish. Instead, she was into the cupboard behind her. Somewhere in here was an old phone that she had bought for the kids when they were little, what they call on *Line of Duty* a burner phone. Or as most people she knew called them, a top-up. This adventure was turning fun. She now had a new email and was using a phone number that no one else knew she had. A regular little spy. The name's Smith, Anne Smith! She typed the number 08956 36576.

Question number four: *Your Country of Residence*. She had no option. There was no multiple choice or phone a friend on this one. Christleton was definitely in England. Unless it was in the United Kingdom. There was no drop-down menu; she would have to make a decision. She believed she was English. If England played Scotland at football, she shouted, quite loudly, for England. She would go for England.

This was a tough one; she wasn't sure. The first three she knew she had right but this one was fifty/fifty. England it was. She took a mouthful of Chardonnay, not everyone's choice of drink when sitting A-level Geography (Anne had decided that completing the form was like resitting her A-levels), and moved to the next question.

Question number five: *Why would you like to hire a genealogist?* Nooooo. Just as everything was going so well. All the answers to date had been black and white, yes or no, plus or minus, and then just as she was gaining her confidence, they slip an essay question in. Bugger. Anne checked to see how much Chardonnay she had left in the bottle but decided she couldn't open another one. She wouldn't remember doing this tomorrow if she had another bottle. She didn't like leaving a half-bottle of wine in the fridge overnight as it never tasted the same the next day.

Firstly, she had to ensure she knew her terms and so googled 'genealogist'.

'A person who traces or studies lines of family descent'. That was pretty straightforward, but she wanted to double-check and so looked the word up in the Cambridge Dictionary.

'Someone who studies genealogy'. She didn't think she had ever seen a greater waste of technology, time, effort, bits and bytes or computer memory. *That has to be the world's worst definition of a word.* She tried one more site but this time tried genealogy, not genealogist, and used the Free Dictionary. They defined genealogy as:

'The history of families from generation to generation. i.e., the genealogy of the royal house of Tudor'. *That's better,* she thought. *I now know exactly what the question is asking. I just need to answer it.*

Anne started to type her answer.

'When we were little, my brother…' She stopped. That's not right; they don't want to know that. After a slight pause, she deleted her first attempt and typed:

'My dad once told us all that he didn't…' Anne was still unhappy. She picked her empty glass up and raised it to her lips before replacing it on the coaster. Pavlov would have been proud. *If I don't get this right this time, that's it. I'm off to bed.*

She typed.

'There are some gaps evident in my family tree and I would like to try and fill them in.' There, simple and straightforward. They don't need to know the background or the emotional side of events. Just give me the scientific approach. Anne told herself that she was going to keep this exercise private until she saw some results. This was her baby, no one else's, and she had no idea if it was going to be a boy or a girl.

Question number six: *Who referred you to us?* This was an easy one, but she wouldn't use a name.

She typed: 'My husband.'

Question number seven, which was more of a disclaimer than a question, asked: *Would you like to receive weekly genealogical research tips? We will send expert weekly genealogical tips to you if you have opted to receive our newsletter.*

Anne mused, *I haven't opted for the newsletter so that means I won't get the tips. But I want the tips not the newsletter, so do I tick the yes box or the no box?* Anne was getting so tired that she just ticked yes. It was past her bedtime, and she could hear the duvet calling her name.

The following morning, Anne took her life, and those of all her ancestors, into her own hands and pressed the submit button. Her details were pinging all around the virtual world now and later that day she received an email back from the online company. They told her that they had found her details and that her DNA test had already been paid for and could she either provide a blood or saliva sample using the tools she would receive through the post, snail mail, in the next couple of days. While she was waiting for the DNA test and equipment, and ultimately the results, she could use the online tools to start her search for her family tree.

All very exciting but she still didn't look on the website again until, several days later, she was prompted by the rattle of the letterbox. Tools and equipment, she scoffed. Basically, she had to either bleed or spit into a little test tube-type bottle, seal it and send it back. It was hardly A-level Chemistry. She logged back on to the website using the new email she had set up, should just this occasion arise. This was when she realised that if she was going to do this properly, she had days of work ahead of her. Just what she needed really, for those dark nights when Colin was away. She read the first paragraph about gathering information.

'The first step in building a family tree is gathering the records and information you already have. These records tend to be most useful:

Family group sheets, pedigree charts, and books of remembrance

- Family Bibles
- Journals, diaries, and letters
- Photographs
- Obituaries and newspaper clippings
- Birth, marriage, and death certificates

If you'd like to organize information in a paper chart before entering it online, download our free family group sheet or pedigree chart. Our many charts are available for free.

Interviewing an older biological relative can help you gather information about your ancestors. Be sure to take notes. Members of your family may remember important details or have family heirlooms, records, or photos that can help you.'

Oh, my sweet Jesus, thought Anne. *Where and how do I start this? What's a pedigree chart and why would I need a Holy Bible? This is a very American website or they wouldn't spell organise with a z.* Being practical and knowing that it would take less effort, Anne spat into the bottle instead and headed for the post office. She would have to pass Waitrose on the way and could nip in for a bottle of wine for later. She believed she needed wine before attempting to start this exercise.

Post office, Waitrose, little walk around the green and back home. It was set in motion now; her saliva was zooming off to some laboratory in London. She had decided that the best way to set about gathering the data she needed would be to go to the font of all knowledge; no, not Google. She would 'interview an older biological relative', or as she liked to call the process, 'talk to Mum'.

Singapore and Hong Kong

1959

Ginger got two weeks' jankers for losing his kit plus the cost of buying another plus the loss of the price of his non-existent purchase, the very pretty sister who may or may not be somewhere in Colombo or may have been a figment of Fernando's vivid imagination (if his name had ever been Fernando). The last week of October loomed and the approach to Singapore was the worst two days on board ship. The *Empire Fowey* got caught up in the tail end of a typhoon.

"Why's it called a typhoon then?" asked a very green-looking Jock. The three bunkmates were all lying on their beds; in fact, if you looked around the rest of the bunks, anyone who wasn't on duty was also trying to keep still. There was an unenviable smell of vomit, sweat and urine, in that order of strength.

"What does it matter what it's called if it's causing this?" answered Ginger. The whole room tilted to what seemed like 45 degrees and then fell the opposite way. The whole boat was bobbing on the Indian Ocean like a rubber duck in a child's bath. There was the sound of retching from the heads, the naval term for the toilets, as more and more men, more used to the land staying still beneath their feet, succumbed to the pleasures of sea sickness. Rocky was one of the lucky ones.

Although he had never been any further than in a rowing boat with Lizzie Prescott, now Lizzie Holmes, on Taylor Park boating pond, he had found his sea legs. The voyage had been a pleasant one to start with but as the boat got further and further into the tropics, they became the victims of extreme weather conditions, far removed from the English Channel. More and more soldiers were becoming ill. Rocky was only one of six men who had made breakfast that morning. He was lying with his mates on the bunks but was doing so more out of social needs than the requirement to keep as still as possible.

Rocky decided to educate his two mates, thus keeping their minds off the fact that, although they had nothing left in their stomachs to resurrect, that wasn't stopping their bodies from attempting to rip off the linings off their intestines and bring that up as well.

"Okay, lads, do you know the difference between a typhoon, a hurricane and a cyclone?" The groans and moans fed back to Rocky suggested that they didn't know.

"Well, the short answer is that there is no difference."

"Then why are you bloody asking, you smart git," answered a voice from the cheap seats.

"Got a point," said Jock. Ginger just moaned and rolled onto his side. The top bunk was by far the safest place to be during a severe bout of sickness. Rocky made sure he was completely under the slats of the bunk above him before he carried on, undeterred.

"They are all organised storm systems that form over warm ocean waters." Since his tutorial on the Suez, Rocky had become something of a 'go-to' to settle arguments and was known by some as the Headmaster, a nickname that only lasted for a few weeks. Rocky was easier to remember and shorter, an army essential. He continued.

"Where there are areas of low pressure, and don't ask me why there are areas of low pressure, because I didn't read that, the winds start to swirl and spin around up to seventy or eighty miles an hour. It's like a roundabout at the fairground."

Jock was biting. He liked it when Rocky could tell them stuff they didn't know. He soon forgot it, but he still liked the idea of learning even if his retention skills were that of a small jellyfish.

"So, why the three names then?"

"It depends where in the world you are. Around here, China, Japan, Malaysia, Singapore, they call them typhoons. In America, the Caribbean and, say, Mexico way, they call them hurricanes. In Australia and in the southern Indian Ocean across to Africa, they call them cyclones. So, they're all the same thing, just different names."

Ginger had had enough. He was ill, he was still smarting from his loss in Colombo, he had been peeling spuds for ten days, and Rocky wouldn't shut the fuck up.

"So, Headmaster, what you're telling us is that we're in the middle of a fucking great storm and it's making us all sick. I don't know about Rocky Holmes, you should be fucking

Sherlock Holmes." This got a good laugh considering most were too frightened to even open their mouths.

Rocky had to answer, or he would lose face.

"Just a spot of education for you, mate. Doesn't hurt to know what you're talking about." Someone jumped off his bunk and ran for the head but didn't make it. He went for a mop and bucket instead. There were many gagging noises and Rocky hoped it wouldn't start a chain reaction.

Rocky continued.

"The Americans have started naming their hurricanes. This year, they've had a Gracie, a Debbie and a Flora."

Quick as a flash, Jock said, "This year, I've had an Annie, a Dora and a Martha, but for God's sake don't tell them about each other." Even though the room was full of sick and ailing men, this got a roar of approval from Jock's compatriots and Jock grew an extra inch with pride. There was a shout from above, "Land ahoy," and Rocky threw himself off his bunk, avoiding the spillage as best as he could.

"Come on, lads. Let's take a look at Singapore."

"It can't be any worse for me than Colombo," said Ginger, and with the seal of approval from their leading man, the three, now close friends, made their way up the stairs onto deck. This part of the journey had taken nine days. It could have been done quicker but there wasn't really a rush. The men would get the opportunity of a short stay in Singapore before finishing the last leg of their journey on to Hong Kong. They had been on board ship for just over four weeks with a planned docking in Hong Kong on the 9th of November 1959.

Once on deck, the shipmates could see the port of Singapore through the sea haze.

"It looks like a magic land," said Jock.

Rocky replied. "Ginger thought Colombo was a magic land. Alakazam, and his uniform just disappeared."

Rocky and Jock nearly fell overboard, they laughed so hard at that one, and even Ginger allowed himself a smile. He replied, "Well, Singapore won't be magic for me as I've had me shore leave revoked. Something about it being for my own good. What are you two up to?"

"It's a quick turnaround here, mate," said Jock. "Six hours only and then straight back and it's from 10am until 4pm, so hardly the high life." The ship docked at Singapore harbour at 7.20am local time. The harbour itself was called Keppel Harbour and was half a mile away from the regular cargo shipping lanes. They would be restocking with essentials, especially fresh water, followed by a four-hour maintenance check and then they would be on their way again to Hong Kong.

Rocky and Jock had a quieter time in Singapore than they did in Colombo. The place was a mass of activity with no room to move. The local port was littered with the Singaporean fishing and cargo boats called *tongkangs* and *twakows*. *Tongkang* refers to several kinds of boats used to carry goods along rivers and the shoreline in south-east Asia, harking back to the fourteenth century. They are unmotorised open cargo boats propelled by a variety of methods including punt poles, rowing or sails.

The *twakow*, meanwhile, is the traditional Singaporean boat and is known as 'the Forgotten Workhorse of Singapore'. Flatter in appearance, with the look of an English barge, the *twakow* was responsible for moving heavier loads around the ports, some capable of holding up to fifty tonnes of cargo. Rocky and Jock were fascinated but with a gang of twenty other 'squaddies', they were less interested in local cargo and fishing boats and more interested in the infamous bar called 'Raffles'. It was an hour-and-a-half trek, but they had all heard so much about Raffles that it would have been a sin to not try and visit the famous hotel and bar.

The bar, along with many of the other local buildings, had a dirty whitewashed look, but Raffles was far more ornate and decorative than the average bar. A covered terraced area ran around the perimeter of the bar holding a covered walkway with arches cut into the walls every ten yards. It reminded Rocky of a Foreign Legion fort that he had seen in a Laurel and Hardy short back home.

Raffles Hotel and bar is named after Stamford Raffles, a British statesman who served as Lieutenant-Governor of the Dutch East Indies in the early 1800s. Raffles the man is the founder of modern Singapore. Raffles the hotel and bar claims to be the founder of the Singapore Sling, the cocktail, which Rocky and Jock particularly wanted to try. The group of baying, loud British soldiers approached the front of the Raffles Hotel. There were simply too many of them and the doorman was having none of it.

"Come on, mate, I've come all the way from Wigan for a Singapore Sling," one hopeful shouted from the back.

"Yeah, give us a break. The Pieman didn't even know what one was until I told him last night," shouted the first caller's mate. Anyone who came from anywhere near Wigan adopted a nickname linked to some form of pie. This was a reference to the 1926 General Strike when workers went on strike due to the poor pay and working conditions in the coal mines of the day. The people of Wigan were the first to break the strike as their families were essentially starving to death. This led to miners of the neighbouring town of Leigh (known as Leythers) to refer to people from Wigan as 'pie eaters', them having, in effect, been forced to 'eat humble pie' and return to work.

The lone lad from Wigan on the *Empire Fowey* would for the next two years only be known as 'the Pieman'. In all honesty, there wasn't one man on board the ship who had ever tasted a Singapore Sling, but they all knew they wanted one. Rocky could see where this situation was heading and, after their experience with Fernando in Colombo, did not want another scrape with either the locals or the local authority.

"Come on, Jock, we're not getting in here without some bother. Let's break away and find a quieter place. My guess is everywhere will be selling this Singapore Sling drink anyway. Come on, let's head back to the main walkway where we came in. I don't want to get lost. This place is a maze." The two servicemen left the throng harassing the doorman, who now had several other doormen and a member of the Singapore police with him as well. Rocky and Jock walked for about fifteen minutes, taking in the sights.

Jock decided he was hungry.

"Rocky, are you hungry?" he asked. They were both at that age when they were always hungry, and no matter what they ate, they never put weight on.

"Always," replied the lad from St Helens, who was turning a skin colour that could no longer be described as 'just come out from under a rock'. "What about that place over there?

That place looks all right" The Islamic restaurant had been in Singapore since opening in 1921 and was especially famed for its biryani dishes. Not that Rocky or Jock would have known this. It simply looked quite splendid from its position on North Bridge Road and had served the sultans of Brunei, Johor and Perak – literally providing meals fit for a king.

The restaurant itself was on two floors. The upper had beautiful blue wooden arched shutters looking out over the local mosque, offset by the thick green brickwork encasing the ground floor. It shone out like a beacon from its humble family origins on the ordinary Singapore street and caught Rocky's eye as he roamed looking for a bite to eat, slightly overwhelmed by the hordes of people and choice of establishments.

"What's Islamic food like, Rocky?" asked Jock.

"We are about to find out," came back the reply, "but I think it's curry!"

Invited in by a staff member hawking on the street, they wandered into an Aladdin's cave of an interior. The colours were vibrant reds and dark rich blues, with historic religious pictures festooning the walls. Old dark wooden tables set out in twos and fours invited the lads to take a seat.

"I know what I'm ordering first," said Jock, and promptly asked for, "Two Singapore Slings, please, waiter and I like to taste the Sling." Jock laughed and Rocky joined him. Neither of the two gentlemen had the first idea of what went into a Singapore Sling, and while Raffles claimed to have invented the drink, virtually every bar, club, restaurant and hotel did their own version of one. That was unless you chose an Islamic restaurant.

The waiter just shook his head at the two squaddies.

"What are you shaking your head at, mate? Just get the drinks," said Jock. It was then that it dawned on Rocky. He realised that some religions, and he thought Islam was one of them, were prohibited from even smelling alcohol.

Rocky said, "We've buggered this up, Jock. We've come into one of the few places that won't serve us alcohol because it's against their religion." All the other clientele were local men, and they were all looking at Rocky and Jock as though they were two Englishmen who had wandered into a halal restaurant in Singapore by mistake, which is just about exactly what they had done. They quickly got the picture menu and pointed at two soft drinks and two chicken biryanis, the cheapest meal on the menu.

Luckily, the place they had chosen was a high throughput restaurant and the turnover at all the tables was quick, with men coming and going regularly in the time they were there. The food arrived, along with two mango drinks.

"What have you got us, Rocky?"

"You're confusing me with a man who gives a shit," replied his so-called mate. "It's rice and chicken and fruit juice. Let's eat it and find a bar." Which is exactly what they did, but not until they had really enjoyed the rich and spicy food that had been placed in front of them. In fact, they loved the aromatic rice so much that they took a bag away with them both to eat on the road as they continued their short tour of the bars of Singapore. Not long after, they were sat at a tiny bar thirty minutes closer to the ship. They didn't want to be late back and be on jankers with Ginger. The bar was that small and dingy that the owners hadn't even bothered naming the place. They at long last got their version of a Singapore Sling.

Now the history of the drink is interesting, although this was a little history that Rocky had never bothered researching at Eccleston Library before leaving for his National Service. The Singapore Sling, widely regarded as the national drink, was first created in 1915 by Raffles bartender Ngiam Tong Boon. Primarily a gin-based cocktail, the Singapore Sling also contains pineapple juice, lime juice, curaçao and Bénédictine. Giving it the pretty pink hue are grenadine and cherry liqueur.

The bartender Ngiam deliberately chose to give the cocktail this rosy colour for the following reason. After the turn of the century in colonial Singapore, Raffles was the gathering place for the community – and Long Bar was the watering hole. It was common to see gentlemen nursing glasses of gin or whisky. Unfortunately for the ladies, etiquette dictated that they could not consume alcohol in public. So, for the sake of modesty, teas and fruit juices were their beverages of choice.

Ever insightful, the Raffles bartender saw a niche in the market and decided to create a cocktail that looked like plain fruit juice but was actually infused with gin and liqueurs. The bright marketeer made the beverage pink to give it a feminine flair that, together with the use of clear alcohol, led people to think it was a socially acceptable drink for women. With that, the Singapore Sling was born.

The bar staff serving Rocky and Jock wouldn't have known curaçao and Bénédictine from Bob Hope and Bing Crosby. So, our two heroes had gin and pineapple juice with an umbrella and some cherries in it to try and at least make it the correct colour, if not the correct taste.

"Not much to this," said Rocky. "I think I'll stick to a pint of mild when I get home." There may not have been much to them, but they both managed six each in the next two hours before having to run back to the ship before jankers beckoned. They were experiencing the world one drink at a time and soon they would be in Hong Kong, where Rocky would receive a letter. A letter that would change his life. A letter that, after reading, meant he would never be the same man again.

Burnley, Lancashire

1936

Time moved on in the small town of Burnley in Lancashire as May made way for a mixed three months of summer. There were many rainy days in a humid hazy June; July was better but the north-west experienced one particular spectacular thunderstorm that lit the night sky around Gawthorpe Hall and reminded many people of the newsreels of the 4th of July celebrations in the States; but by the time August rolled in, the English summer had exploded into bright yellow sunshine and long days of heat were followed by sticky longer nights.

For Elsie Scott, every day was a day filled with sunshine as her relationship bloomed as magnificently as the red roses in the gardens of the manor house. James Knowles may well have been based in London but would manipulate as many visits around the country as his employers would endure. If he was on the road, he would ensure he spent at least some part of a day up in Burnley and he became a regular visitor to the back-door entrance of Gawthorpe.

He didn't have a lot of money but his pay in comparison to the staff of the house was far superior and he made sure that Mrs Dawson and Cook were always on his side with little sweeteners of presents such as chocolates or something as simple as a jar of cocoa powder. He was not brought up anybody's fool, was Mr Knowles. He would arrive with something for the kitchen and was invariably able to charm Elsie away for an hour or two minimum as long as she made up her time. Mr Dawson didn't take to James quite as well as the ladies did, but his occasional sweetener would be something a little stronger.

They soon developed a system of phone calls, knowing that it was a rare time when either Lord or Lady Shuttleworth would answer the telephone first; after all, what were the staff for, so it was never a complete surprise when he turned up at the back door. If the Shuttleworths were about, Elsie would meet James in the town; otherwise, he would roar around the house in a car taken from one of the garages where he was working. He was always very generous with the car, allowing others to drive it as long as they stayed on the estate or alternatively taking people for drives in the surrounding countryside. He often felt he wasn't just trying to win Elsie over but the entire household. She was worth it, though, as he was falling hard for the feisty young girl, who for the times kept him well and truly on his guard.

Elsie for her part also kept herself on her guard. She would admit to Dot several times in the small dark hours of the night in the tiny bedroom they shared that she was falling for James but remained tight-lipped when discussing her feelings with everyone else. She was fighting the emotions of love because she didn't believe she deserved them and that no good could come from her 'getting above herself'. Nevertheless, she wasn't cold with him when she and James managed to grab some time alone together and they had now kissed on several occasions, and the warm glow emanating from her lower belly was telling her something was right about him. She wouldn't allow herself to think the L word, but it was taking shape over those summer months.

For James's part, he knew he was the elder statesman in the relationship, but Elsie had a good head on her shoulders, confident and strong-willed. His relationship record was erratic, some more serious than others, but none had ever felt as strong as the feelings he held for Elsie. As far as James was concerned, he was biding his time until he could get the promotion he'd been looking for. The next level up the job ladder would be more management and far less travel and his task would be enticing Elsie down to the smoke of London, although the smoke of the industrialised north was far worse, but not so much in Burnley. He just had one or two problems to iron out first.

Plus, James took an interest in world affairs and Germany were making moves on Continental Europe. In March of that year, Germany had retaken the Rhineland in direct conflict with the Treaty of Versailles. Then during the Olympics, held in Berlin in August 1936, there had been a direct show of power to the rest of the world. At least that's what everyone was saying. Both Hitler and Mussolini sent aid and troops to support the Nationalist party in the Spanish Civil War, and James was sure that world war was brewing again. Did he really want to raise a family in this climate?

The weather started to cool, and the summer made way for early autumn. It was Elsie's favourite season of the year as she loved the brown, reds and golds of the leaves and bushes as they turned. Cook didn't like autumn much as she said everything was dying, but Elsie chose to see everything as going to sleep and resting for the new year. Gawthorpe Manor turned into a cornucopia of colours, and the gardens, meadows, copses and woods became golden. Elsie saw this as a sign for the way her life was heading. Cook's viewpoint would come back to haunt Elsie several times in the future.

By early October, the new *Romeo and Juliet* film starring Norma Shearer and Leslie Howard and directed by George Cukor had found its way to Burnley. Two young lovers thrown together from different warring families who should never have fallen in love. It was a must for Elsie, so when James turned up on Saturday, 10th October, she knew exactly where they would be going that night. It was the same morning that James had ominously read in the *London Gazette* that women over the age of eighteen would be employed filling three-inch mortar bombs. It was the first time since the Great War that women could be employed in munitions factories.

By now, they had managed to escape the chaperone that was the energetic Dot, plus the fact that the film was getting mixed reviews had persuaded her that it wasn't worth her hard-earned pennies. 'Not one for the masses,' claimed one local paper, while another said, 'Ornate but not garish, extravagant but in perfect taste, expansive but never overwhelming, the picture reflects great credit upon its producers and upon the screen as a whole.' This was an extract from a rave review copied from *The New York Times* and used in a London paper brought up to Burnley by James. Dot trusted the local press far more than any New York reporter and told Elsie she didn't really want to see it but she would keep her company if she wanted. Elsie politely declined the offer of company.

Sat in the dark in the sixpenny seats, the two lovers held hands and whispered promises that neither could keep. It was during the film that James told Elsie for the first time that 'he loved her'. Elsie didn't immediately reply, and James thought he had measured the mood incorrectly and fretted through the remaining thirty minutes of the film. He couldn't concentrate, not watching it or paying attention to the sad ending until he saw the tears in Elsie's eyes. Outside, they were silent, only speaking back in the car when James pushed his claim for love.

"What made you cry, Elsie? Was it the film or my declaration of love? Are you not ready yet?" The questions flew from James's mouth like shots from a sniper's rifle. Elsie composed herself before answering, worrying James all over again.

"I cried because I'm happy. No one has ever told me they love me before, not even my mum and dad. Words like love aren't used much where I was raised. Then Romeo and Juliet dying for each other just after you've told me you love me set me off again. And in answer to your final question, yes, I'm ready, as I love you too." James took the lead and they kissed passionately and held onto each other tightly in the car as though their lives depended upon it.

James remained interested in what was happening on the global stage, more so when he was stationed in London than when he was on the road. He read Winston Churchill's speech of Tuesday, 12th November in the Houses of Parliament, vilifying the Baldwin government for the UK's slow response to 'the unwelcome fact' of German rearmament, warning that Britain was entering a new period of danger from what Hitler was orchestrating from Berlin. Churchill also said, "The era of procrastination, of half measures, of soothing and baffling expedients, of delays, is coming to a close," Churchill stated, "In its place, we are entering a period of consequences." James read everything he could about what he perceived as the threat of war and was not reticent to admit that the news frightened him.

On the 14th of November, Hitler announced that Germany would no longer observe the articles in the Treaty of Versailles that had internationalised rivers such as the Rhine, Elbe and Oder so that landlocked countries could have access to the sea. Germany were breaking all agreements and becoming their own international lawmakers. Elsie and James continued their romance.

They saw each other three more times before the Christmas month came around. They spent time walking around the local area talking and getting to know each other properly. They even went shopping together, and James pulled Elsie into a photographer's to 'get himself a keepsake', especially as they had a special offer on. Another time, they managed a very cold picnic that Cook had helped Elsie prepare. Elsie told Dot they were 'proper courting now'.

There was to be a big party at London's Ritz Hotel that the Shuttleworths were attending, and Mr Dawson was attending as his lordship's man, plus the chief maid to her ladyship to dress her for the event. The remaining servants decided that Tuesday, 1st December would be the ideal time for them to have their own small party downstairs. James drove from London on the Monday to work in the Midlands on Tuesday and Wednesday, but this would give him the chance to attend the early Christmas celebration at Gawthorpe Manor; the downstairs of Gawthorpe Manor. In his pocket was a ring.

It wasn't the biggest party that James had ever attended, but it was certainly one of the happiest. They did not have much, but they enjoyed what they had to the fullest. The staff were at their peak during the winter months as the work required to maintain the manor was at a premium. Hawkins, the groundkeeper, was there with three of his lads; Mrs Dawson and Cook held pride of place at the head of the table, and there were four maids, two of whom were Elsie and Dot, plus two new recruits fresh from school in Accrington called Margaret and Maud. James was the only outsider, but he soon became an insider by supplying a crate of beer for the lads and two bottles of fizzy wine for those who didn't drink beer.

Cook had performed a small miracle with a roast chicken and veggies from the garden and had even had time to make a small Christmas pudding. Crackers and party hats had been provided by the Shuttleworths, although no one had told them. The beer and fizz flowed, and James and Elsie held hands under the table when they could. After sharing the pudding out, James got the lucky halfpenny that Cook had hidden in the mix; they couldn't afford a sixpence.

"Make a wish then," shouted Cook. "That's what you do when you win the prize in the Christmas pudding. Make a wish, go on." Cook had liberated most of a bottle of wine and started chanting, "Make a wish, make a wish, make a wish." It wasn't long before everyone joined in. James took hold of the moment like a rabbit caught in a snare. Firstly, standing and pushing his chair away from him with the backs of his legs, he startled everyone, and the chanting stopped until one of the lads burped and they all got a fit of the giggles. James dropped down onto one knee as though he had been shot and produced from his pocket a small box with a flourish that a West End magician would have been proud of.

Flicking the lid of the box open with one practised finger, he asked the ultimate question: "Elsie Scott, will you marry me?"

This was a bolt from the deepest depths of the blue for Elsie. She knew they had expressed their love and had from time to time joked about having kids of their own, but she never expected this. And in front of all the other servants. She couldn't take it in and all she could hear was everyone cheering and shouting. The lads were clapping James on the back, Mrs Dawson was crying, and Cook was trying to get a cork out of another bottle of wine she had somehow found surplus to requirements in the cellar. James was just looking at Elsie; he was still waiting for an answer.

Not a word passed Elsie's lips as she rose from the table, pushed past James and left the kitchen. Seconds later, they could hear the pounding of her feet echoing through the house as she ran up the back stairs. James said to everyone, "You all stay here and continue enjoying yourselves. I'll find Elsie. I obviously shocked her but don't worry, she'll be fine." He quickly followed his love as a loud pop behind him meant Cook had let the cork out of the bottle. Entering the main house, cloaked in darkness apart from a lit candle on the landing of each floor (when the lord and lady were away, costs were kept to a bare minimum and electric lights were rarely used outside of the servants' quarters), James walked slowly up the main stairs. Eventually finding his way to Elsie's room, he rapped hard on the door, receiving no answer.

Opening the door, he leant into the pitch darkness of her room but sensed he was alone. *Where has she gone?* he thought. Retracing his steps, he trotted down the dimly lit main stairs and into the manor's hallway. He was at the entrance to the back stairs, hidden by a panelled door in the wall, when he heard Elsie whisper his name.

"James." It was neither a question nor a statement. It was a plea, and he heard the longing in her voice as he turned and went to find her. The wide stairway created a roomy space beneath and crouched in the darkness, tears streaming down her face, sat Elsie.

"Please tell me what is wrong," he asked, crouching in front of her and pulling her hands down so that he could see her face.

"I'm just in shock," she said. "I thought if you were going to do something like that, you might have warned me."

"I didn't know I was going to do it until I was down on one knee. The moment took me. I looked at you smiling and laughing and looking as beautiful and happy as I have ever seen you and something made me do it. It felt right."

James leant in and kissed Elsie and then proceeded to

kiss away the tears on her cheeks with his lips. She responded and the fire flamed inside her. She knew what was going to happen and welcomed it. It wasn't long before they were making love, right there under the stairs. They were quick and urgent, and Elsie could still hear the party going on downstairs. She would like to say that she enjoyed the first time she ever made love but afterwards all she could remember was pain and a muddle of clothes and the fear of being caught. They dressed quickly and in silence, the momentousness of their lovemaking taking their tongues. What they didn't know, and how could they, was that Elsie had conceived. The first time and she was pregnant.

The second fact they could never possibly have known was that this would be the last evening in their lives they would ever set eyes on each other. The lovers would never meet again.

Old Road, Hampton

2007

A Journal

June 27th
Wednesday. I was going home. Home for me would always be Farnborough where Mum and Dad lived together for a while before Mum raised us and then met Malcolm and then moved to Wandsworth. I'm getting ahead of myself. This story isn't about me, well, it is, but not just me. I'll tell you who I am. That might help. My name is Susan Marie Holmes. My dad is Graham Holmes, and his dad is James Holmes and his dad, well, we don't know who his dad is. That's what Dad says anyway. I think I'll start again.

My name is Susan Holmes and I've just finished university in Exeter and now I'm coming home but not to Mum's. I'm coming home but to Dad's, in Hampton, not Farnborough, I mean, Wandsworth now. This is all very complicated. I just graduated in History; I'm expecting a 2.1. Fantastic, but what do I do now? Since I left home in Farnborough to go and live in Exeter for three years, Mum has got married, again, and moved to Wandsworth. All my friends are in Farnborough and all my new friends have gone back to their hometowns and are spread all over the UK.

I do have some friends in Hampton as we stayed with Dad every weekend growing up, but not particularly close friends. Anyway, that's not the problem. The problem is, what am I going to do with my life? History was great for three years, but I don't want to do it forever. Plus, listen to this, you couldn't make it up. Julie, my older sister, has split up with her boyfriend in Brighton and she's come back to Dad's, and John, my younger brother, has just started a local university in London and has moved in with Dad.

So, Dad and Jayne, my stepmum, are in the front bedroom. Julie has taken my old room next to Dad's, and John has the extension bedroom at the back of the house. Julie wasn't supposed to be breaking up with twatface, that's what Dad called him, twatface, but we're all delighted she's back from Brighton. But the point is, she has my old bedroom that I was coming back for. Mum still thinks it's the best thing for me to do, move in with Dad, so I'll stick to the plan and next stage is getting a job. That's once we've worked out where I sleep! Ha ha. Right, got to get ready now. Exams done, it's party time!

June 30th

Saturday. The world needs to be a lot quieter today than it is. I have a head the size of Gibraltar. What did I drink last night? I don't remember getting home but Holly is here with me, so we must have got each other home. What's Holly doing here? She doesn't live with me. I'll ask her when she crawls out of my bed. Dad said he would be here at twelve, and when Dad says twelve, he'll pootle along to the front door at two minutes to. I don't know how he does it. The trip from Hampton to Exeter isn't an easy one and there's always traffic but he's never been late. I think he must set out the night before and sleep in his car!

What time is it now? Just gone ten so not too bad. I don't have a lot to pack up. I always say that, and Dad and Jayne fall about laughing. Mum always says that my 'not a lot' is most people's 'too much'. If you know what I mean. The journey is three and a half hours on a good day and four hours on a bad one. Unless it's a really bad traffic day, a bad accident or something, in which case all bets are off.

My boyfriend has been with me at university but I'm not sure that was such a clever idea for either of us. And I told him last night. I said, "I'm not too sure this has been a clever idea for us, Ste. What do you think?" He just started crying. He was very drunk. Well, everyone was very drunk. One of those, 'Oh no, it's the last chance we will all be together like this for the rest of our lives' kind of nights. Mum said enjoy it for what it is; Dad said get your CV done. I like a nice balance. I'm enjoying writing in my journal. It's therapeutic. Back to Ste. I think it's off. He followed me to Exeter from Farnborough. I liked the romance of it at eighteen. At twenty-one, I'm wishing I'd been afforded a bit more freedom at uni. It is what it is. He's a nice bloke but needy. I have to do everything. Not as in cooking and cleaning and such, he doesn't live here anyway, but when it comes to making plans or decisions, I have to do it. He's only in Exeter because I picked it for myself.

Sheep and shepherd comes to mind. That's not fair. Sorry, journal. I'm a baaaaad girl. That's a joke by the way. Right, got to get moving. Dad will be here soon, and he will want everything ready to 'load the car'.

July 6th

Friday. So, I'm back at Dad's. Not quite worked out how we all wanted. Julie has my old room, and that lady is not for turning even though she's left home more times than Dad said he's finished playing rugby. I've already had a couple of interviews. I want some money!!!!! I can't live here forever, and the house isn't really set up for three grown-up kids to come back. The original house was just a two-up two-down Victorian cottage. Jayne's mum and dad extended downstairs, putting a kitchen in, because Jayne and Dad bought it off them. Then Dad and Jayne extended it, putting a dining room on the back with another bedroom on top of that.

Anyway, my point is, there is no fourth bedroom for me, and I couldn't share with Julie as it's too small, and there's no way I'm going in with a sweaty eighteen-year-old lad, brother or no brother. So, the old dining room downstairs, which is now a den with the computer and desk and books and a futon couch in, has become my bedroom. Dad has found an old clothes rail for me to hang my clothes up and we're all just going to have to manage. Not that easy as the two original downstairs rooms are only separated by glass double doors, so Dad has put up a curtain rail to separate the rooms properly. Anyone watching the telly until late is virtually in my bedroom with me. Not exactly ideal.

One of my interviews was with a cool marketing company in Richmond, the MOST expensive place in the whole of the UK to live but commutable. Awkward as it's not on the same train line as Hampton but there is an occasional train that goes round the loop. That's Jayne's expression, not mine, but there are a couple of trains a day that go directly into Richmond. The company is called Blue Whale Marketing and their logo is a dark blue whale that you can see through and inside it is a boardroom table with silhouettes of people sat around. Pretty cool. I know it doesn't mean they are any good, but it certainly catches the eye.

They need a receptionist. So glad I studied something relative like History. That's the problem with uni; you might come out with a smart degree, but what do you do with it if it's not practical? Unless you want to be a teacher, which I don't think I do, unless nothing else happens then I may have to want to be a teacher, but I really don't! Dad says just get into employment and see how it goes. Mum says there's always the opportunity of finding something on your journey, but I think she heard that on *The X Factor*.

The interview went well. Vibrant modern office near the top of Richmond Hill. Very young office, I know I'm coming up to twenty-two, but I didn't see anyone really old in there. They all seemed under thirty. Pay is ok, not earth-shattering after three years of study but slightly above the going rate, but that's probably because everything in Richmond costs more than the going rate. I answered all their questions, including the one about what I liked to do in my spare time, and I said, "Socialising."

But it's true, I do like socialising. I'm always with friends and it's not as though I don't like my own company either. I can easily potter around for an evening sorting stuff out in my room. That is, unless my room is the den or study! Julie says she's moving back out soon, going back to Basingstoke where she lived before Brighton before coming back before going to Brighton, before coming back and going back to Basingstoke. Dad says we are all on pieces of elastic and just as we get too far away, spring back to Old Road.

I don't know what she means by soon, but it can't be soon enough. The futon is a double and comfortable enough, but the room still has to be used by others and for some reason I just don't feel comfortable at night lying downstairs when everyone else in the house is upstairs. I don't get spooked easily but Jayne told me that when she was a young girl they got burgled, and she'll never forget walking back into the house after other people had been through all their things. Apparently her mum, Mary, lost a lot of jewellery in the robbery. Not expensive stuff but of sentimental value that she simply never got back. So, I'm laying on the futon at night thinking about burglars. Not conducive to a good night's sleep. Plus, you know what it's like when your mind starts working in the middle of the night. I come up with all sorts of scenarios and hear all sorts of noises. The other night, I thought I heard a ball bouncing on the wooden floor but when I woke properly, it had gone. Stupid dream more like. That's what I'm telling myself.

July 12th

Thursday. Got the job, got the job, got the job! Did I tell you, I GOT THE JOB! I start Monday, next Monday, 16th. They were impressed with my maturity and the fact that I held down part-time jobs all the way through uni. Dad said that would work in my favour, but I never thought that at the time. Not only do I start Monday but tomorrow night, which does happen to be Friday the 13th, I'm meeting all the Blue Whale girls (that doesn't sound very nice) for a couple of drinks at All Bar One in Richmond. I absolutely have to be on my best behaviour. I can have a drink and a dance but must restrict the dancing to the dance floor and not the tables. I'm joking!

I'm chuffed. I thought the interview had gone well but you never can tell for sure. The girls I'm meeting are Melody, Clarissa and Megan. Why does everyone have such cool names except me? They're all a little older as well. Mid-twenties, I would say, and Megan has been married and divorced already. They have different concepts around boyfriends than I have. They are all seeing people apparently, not boyfriend/girlfriend, just seeing. I'm starting to think I'm a little old-fashioned in my outlook. We will see. I'm off to get ready, something short and sexy for my first night out in Richmond. Not too sexy but I want to feel good. Let you know Saturday how it goes.

July 14th

Saturday. Too tired to write much today, plus Dad is on the warpath. Perhaps tomorrow.

July 18th

Wednesday. Sorry, been busy. Firstly, I'll have to tell you all about last Friday. My first lesson of going out in Richmond with a group of older girls I hardly know is, and I'm sure you've seen this on the adverts on the telly, 'Learn to say NO!' I didn't get drunk, but I was well on the way. Megan was the worst, and the best, I suppose. It's as if her getting married young, getting divorced young and having a young child being looked after by her mum has given her licence to be chief party girl. She went for it. If she was waiting for someone else to buy a round, she went and got a shot for herself while she was waiting. And she nearly caused a fight. She says she didn't but tell that to the two blokes who were launching into each other outside the Pitcher and Piano. She wore what Dad would call a pelmet – I think that's the spelling – rather than a skirt. He dropped me off and said her skirt was so short that you could see next week's washing.

When I say worst and best, what I mean is she was just out for a good time and a laugh. She would flirt and chat to lads but that was it. Once bit, I suppose. She attracted lads like ants round sugar, but she says she 'never leads them on'. It still didn't stop the bouncers stopping those two she'd been talking to from knocking lumps off each other. You'd think I'd be used to this coming back from a university town like Exeter, but there is an air of privilege around Richmond that makes people think they can do just whatever they want. So, she was the worst in our little gang, until you drop your perspective.

She was also the best, though, because she made me feel the most welcome. Taking me to the bar with her, involving me in conversations, asking about me and my life at uni, what I wanted to do with my life and generally not leaving me on my own and having my back. So, the best as well. And when it got to eleven, she was off.

"I promised Mum I'd be back by half eleven and that's what time I'll be. She's got Tiffany for me, and I can't risk pissing her off for one more drink. Good night, luvvie, and I'll see you Monday morning for day one in the *Big Brother* house." She said that last bit like the bloke off the telly programme and it made me laugh.

The other two girls, Melody and Clarissa, were obviously mates and stuck together like Richard and Judy. Once Meg had gone home, we went on to a grotty little club. I found out that these two worked in sales support together, and what they didn't know about Blue Whale wasn't worth knowing. I wasn't too sure what sales support actually do, so I had to ask Dad on Sunday. He was still a bit annoyed with me and was sulking a bit. What is it about men? They'll go out on a rugby pitch and batter each other to a pulp then have a pint later as though nothing had happened. I get in an hour late without a phone call and I get the sulks for forty-eight hours.

Back to Friday. The club was called Viva and was full of young girls, yes, even younger than me, and men in their late twenties and early thirties and some much older than that. My future beckoned and I didn't realise until Saturday that I didn't much like where it was taking me. I had a fun time, snogged a bloke, didn't get his name, and then managed to get into a taxi while Melody and Clarissa shared one going to Clapham as they lived close together. I said I would be home not much after midnight as I never intended clubbing it, going out, out. It was nearly 3am when I got in and the cab driver was a bit creepy.

The good news is, when your bedroom is on the ground floor, you can slip into your room without waking anyone up, hopefully. The bad news is that after drinking all night I was going to need the bathroom, across what was left of it, and would have to keep creeping up and downstairs. No downstairs bathroom in a Victorian cottage. The final negative was Dad slept like a ninja when any of us were out, to be fair to him, male or female, and had been waiting for me to get in. I was nearly twenty-two, for God's sake. I could go clubbing on a Friday if I wanted to! He says he has no objection to me going clubbing just so long as he knows and then doesn't worry when we don't get in on time.

I believe my older brother, Alan, once rang Dad up saying one of his friends had taken an overdose and he had to stay with them. And he was only seventeen. I hope I don't have to take a call like that if I ever have kids. So, Ninja Dad gets up, takes one look at me and utters the immortal words, "Get yourself to bed and we can talk about this in the morning." Well, there's a sedative for a good night's sleep if I ever heard one.

Another problem with having a downstairs bedroom with a flimsy door and a curtain between you and the world is that the world tends to start up next morning earlier than you do after a night clubbing in Richmond. But I wasn't frightened last night and at least slept, although sleep after a night out isn't all it's cracked up to be. Saturday was a blur. I had a conversation with Dad about 'letting him know', and I know he was only being reasonable but if he knew half of what we got up to in Exeter, he'd look greyer than John Major.

Sunday, I went to Mum's but got back early as I had to plan for Monday morning. Bed first, up first, out of the house first, these were all first firsts for me. Train was on time, and I found myself at the office in Richmond before they had opened up and ended up in Costa reading *The Book Thief* by Markus Zusak. I love those stories set against real historical events, well, I guess I would, wouldn't I, after reading History at uni.

The first day at Blue Whale was more of a blur than Saturday was after clubbing it Friday. But don't take this the wrong way. I'm all over it now. When I was at uni, I waited on in a busy hotel restaurant, I worked at Royal Ascot and Epsom, not on Derby Day but Derby week, and so I'm used to customer service-type pressure. I knew that good prompt smiley service at these events would result in a healthy tip, and I invariably got them.

By close of play today, Wednesday night, I had the phone system mastered, the meeting bookings sorted and was literally looking for work. I hate being idle, especially at work, nothing worse. Megan looks like being a friend and while Clarissa and Melody are not unfriendly, I'm just on reception, if you know what I mean. So, overall, not a bad start.

July 21st

Saturday. Rest of the week at work went ok. Home not so good. Thursday night, I woke up frightened. Still on the futon in the back room downstairs. There is a blocked-up fireplace that is never used as a hearth anymore, but I'm sure I heard an animal or something in there. Friday, went out straight from work. Not out out, just out. Home on time, so all good. Then something woke me in the night again and the computer fired up on the desk for no reason. When I say fired up, I mean it was already on, but the screen just lit up and the screensaver, some mountains somewhere, brightened up the whole room. I put my blouse over it that I had taken off earlier but it slipped off and so I turned and faced the wall.

I think I heard a squeak. God, I hope we don't have a bloody mouse. Going to Mum's tonight so I'll get a better night's sleep there, even if I do sleep with the dog, Bruno.

July 22nd
Sunday. Went to bed early again. In fact, sat on the futon now writing this on the laptop and it's only 8.30pm. Frightened of going to sleep. This is silly, I know, but I'm getting anxious over nothing and then when I wake up in the night downstairs on my own, the bumps and creaks of the house become all sorts in my imagination. I'm being foolish.

July 23rd
Monday. John got in really late last night, Sunday, after playing rugby. Took the pressure off me a bit. Ha ha.

July 26th
Thursday 10am. I'm terrified. I've not gone to work, and John is here with me. Dad and Jayne had to go to work. Do you believe in ghosts? I don't think I do or at least I don't think I did.

I woke up in the small hours of Tuesday morning. It was pitch black. The computer screen had lit up again. Dad said it must be a glitch. He'd have a look at it at the weekend. I lay there on my back, eyes screwed shut, when I heard a banging against the wall to the right of the chimney breast. At least it was as far away in the room as it could be, diagonally opposite. Trust me, though, these aren't big rooms. It was a soft, rhythmic banging: badaam, pause, badaam, pause, badaam. I turned away and faced the wall. Not sure whether I fell asleep first or it stopped.

Middle of the night, Wednesday morning. I woke again. Something, whatever it was, was causing me to wake up at around the same time. Computer was turned off tonight so that hadn't come on. I think I would have screamed had that lit up when turned off at the wall. I stayed absolutely still, wondering why I had woken. The hairs on my arms and neck bristled and I swear the room felt cold. Dad had said we must have a mouse, well, I tell you, it was an Arctic mouse because the temperature in that room dropped. I tried to be brave and sensible. Getting out of the bed, I flicked the desk lamp on and, turning around, I almost wet myself. In fact, I think I did.

Looming over me was a dark, crooked shape vaguely in a human form with an elongated body and long arms but tiny legs. Of course there was, it was my own bloody shadow from the lamp I'd just turned on. But that is how frayed my nerves have got. I went out of the room and went upstairs to the bathroom. I tried to make some noise but not too much. If I woke someone up and they wanted to speak to me then great. Julie heard me and went to the bathroom as well. I told her I was scared, and she suggested I get in with her, but it's a tiny single bed and we both had work on Wednesday, so I declined. I felt better for talking to her, got myself a glass of water and went back to bed. I left the lamp on, and it was late when I eventually got off to sleep.

Thursday 2am was the worst. I'll write about it tomorrow. I'm too upset now.

July 27th

Friday. I went back to work today. I couldn't very well tell them in my second week I had a day off because I was haunted, so I had to use the sick note, which I'm not proud of but I don't get paid as I'm on probation anyway. Either way, I couldn't have worked yesterday, that was certainly no lie. I wish I could put down here exactly what's happening to me, but I don't know. And that in itself is scary. They always say that if you know what's wrong and start taking positive action, you feel better for your ills. But I don't know my ills yet.

I'm not a scatty girl and on the whole, pre drinks, pretty well rounded. I think things through and I'm caring and compassionate towards others. I don't take unnecessary risks. For example, as a young kid, if the weather warning in the summer holidays was hot, hot, hot, and there was a news warning about 'wild' swimming without supervision, I just wouldn't do it. So, all my friends were leaping in and out the local ponds or river and I wouldn't go in. If there had been an adult to supervise us then that would have been ok but otherwise, no. I would read an article in the paper about some poor boy getting into difficulty and drowning and that would be it, even though I am a strong swimmer. So, not a risk-taker but not easily rattled either. Or so I thought.

Back to Thursday 2am. Once again, I'm awake, but don't know why. And I wake with a start. I almost sat up bolt upright from my sleeping position. I wasn't screaming but it was worse. I was sort of moaning that tried to turn into a scream, but I stifled it as I woke and came into consciousness. So, I woke moaning. I must have been dreaming but what I don't know, and still don't know as I write this two days later on Friday night.

I get up and go into the kitchen. I have left the lamp on in the study, my bedroom, as I no longer like going to sleep in the dark and certainly don't like waking up from a nightmare in the dark. I get myself a cold glass of water and gulp it down in one before drinking most of a refill, thinking at the time that this will mean another rise later in the night for the bathroom. Taking what's left, I go down the dark hallway and almost scuttle back into my bedroom from the dark to the shaded light of the orange lamp on the desk. Not a lamp in my mind anymore but more a creator of shadow creatures.

I sat on the futon bed, feet on the floor, which means I'm facing towards the side of the house that joins onto number 39, where the chimney breast on the unused fireplace is situated. It's July so my PJs are a little pair of shorts and top, a silky set from Marks. But the room is hot, old Victorian cottage with thick brick walls, absorbs the heat during the day and releases it during the night. But this is how it happened; I swear.

From my ankles upwards, I started to feel goosebumps form and travel up my body in a wave. The tiny hairs on my legs twitched upright and then my arms and neck. I whimpered, I remember whimpering. It was like a cold breeze had come in from outside and swept over me, like you see a flag fluttering in a wind. I have never felt so frightened in my entire life. You have heard the expression, 'frozen to the spot'. Well, that was me.

My hand holding the glass trembled and then from behind the desk, in the corner of the room, came the unmistakable sound of something scraping down the wall. Not my side of the wall but the other side, or even worse, inside the wall. It was ever so gentle, like a tool running up and down a bumpy wall, but then it got more urgent and aggressive before stopping altogether. I gasped.

Then the worst noise of all. Faint at first so I couldn't really hear it, but I heard a ball bouncing, same as a few nights ago. Rhythmic, consistent, badaam, badaam, badaam. Throw, double bounce, catch. Throw, double bounce, catch. Not sure if that's a now thought or I thought it at the time. But it wasn't in the room with me, it sounded outside the room.

Finally, what got me to move and do something. The ball started to bounce again, but on the wooden floor, in the same room, right next to me. Drop, bounce, catch. Drop, bounce, catch. And then I heard a child's voice speak. I ran. Out the room, up the stairs, I kept going straight into John's room and jumped into bed with him. I was shaking like a wet dog. Eventually, he managed to make sense of what I was trying to tell him and with no fear whatsoever went downstairs and into my bedroom-cum-study. I followed him halfway down the stairs and sat on one just where Robin from *The Muppets* would have sat. I don't know why I'm trying to be funny. Coping mechanism, I guess.

"Nothing in here, sis," he said. I heard doors open above me.

"What the bloody hell is going on?" asked a bleary-eyed Dad.

"Nothing, nothing, honestly," I answered. John came back out of my room and told Dad that I had been spooked by something. Dad asked me to go back to bed but I wouldn't. Wouldn't, more like I couldn't. I would never sleep in that room again.

"Susan, please top and tail with John and we'll sort this out in the morning." Dad could see by how pale I looked that something had genuinely frightened me. Thursday morning, Dad had gone to work, and I'd decided I had to stay home. I hadn't slept a wink since the ball and couldn't get the noise from my head. Now, Friday night, I'm writing this from Julie's room as she's gone back to Basingstoke. Dad and I have had a long chat about 'Ballgate' as John has kindly named it.

Dad thinks the pressure of getting through my finals and then the emotion of leaving Exeter and having to come back to London and then Julie coming home and displacing me from my room, well, he thinks all of the above are playing on my mind. Then I found a new job and started at Blue Whale, so I suppose he could be right. My subconscious may be working overtime and waking me at night and my imagination is doing the rest. I hear him but I don't really believe it.

I remember the bouncing ball noise. It was clear. What wasn't so clear was the child's voice. If I had to pick, I would say it was a little boy's voice and if I had to hazard another guess, I would say that he said, "Susan." Now that does fit into Dad's version of it's all me. After all, if I heard a voice in my own head, it's highly likely that the owner of the voice would know my name. But I'm not Doctor Jekyll and Mister Hyde! I don't have another version of myself hiding away in there.

I should have spoken to Jayne first, thinking about it. Jayne has lived at 41 Old Road for all of her life. She was born upstairs, as was her dad, and apart from when she went to uni herself and a brief spell in a flat, she has lived here ever since buying the house off her mum and dad, a lovely old couple from the area called Bert and Mary. They sold up to Jayne and retired to the south coast, Bideford, I think. She's told me about the next-door neighbour who died in his bed at number 39. His name was Uncle Ted.

41 Old Road, Hampton

1978

Jayne went back to college after that weekend and didn't have much time to think about Uncle Ted until Easter. Good Friday was 24th March that year, and she had two weeks off lectures and wanted to spend some time being spoiled as an only child. She left her last lecture on the Tuesday, giving herself the best part of three weeks to relax. She had smashed every exam up to that point and had no doubts that her first year was going to be successful. She unpacked her books from the rucksack in the small bedroom that nearly thirty years later Julie and Susan would be fighting over for residency.

Easter that year provided some disappointing weather, cold, but at least it was dry with very little rain and Jayne got the opportunity to spend some time with her best friend, Anna. They just walked through Bushy Park or wrapped up and took picnics to the gardens there. Jayne shared the mystery around Uncle Ted and showed Anna the photo that had fallen from the envelope almost two months ago.

"Do you have any idea who it is?" asked Anna.

"We don't have a clue. There's nothing written on the reverse, not even a year, so we literally have nothing to work with whatsoever. Mum has sent a copy of it to some of Uncle Ted's relatives in Canada, but we have to do it through the solicitors. It's all very mysterious. My dad says we should just leave it all alone, but it is intriguing. In his letter, Uncle Ted says he will be in touch, and I guess that's what this photo is. He's telling us who it was he loved."

Anna sighed and lay on her back on the rough blanket the girls had thrown down by the little brook running through the centre of the park. The wild deer grazed on the other side, with the occasional deep lowing from one of the stags. It was coming into mating season, and you really didn't want to get in the way of their ardour.

Anna said, "It's very romantic. I wish someone would do that for me." Anna worked in Boots the Chemist in Kingston and was a bright blue-eyed chubby girl, lacking confidence through school bullies. Jayne had befriended Anna when finding her crying in the school toilets. They had stayed best friends ever since.

"Do what for you, Anna? We don't know that Uncle Ted did anything romantic. His letter claims he was in love, but that could have been his wife who went off to Canada. And this photo, pretty though the lady is, could be his wife, could be anyone."

"Don't spoil it, Jayne. I have a story in my head of a love that could never be consummated. Lovers who were torn apart through circumstances they could never control. Ted tried to love again but never could and carried that photograph next to his heart for the rest of his days."

Jayne laughed.

"With all due respect," then she remembered that anyone starting a sentence with those words invariably showed no respect at all. "What I mean to say is, that is a load of bollo." The girls would never swear to each other so used their own words and abbreviations to make amends. "If Uncle Ted had a story he wanted us to know, he would have made it clear to Mum or Dad. Probably wouldn't have told me but he would have told one of them two."

Anna replied, "I guess we will never know but for now I'm sticking with my romantic version of life. It's okay for you planning to go off to a posh university, but I'm stuck here selling nasal sprays to dodgy old men." That was one of the traits that Jayne loved about Anna, her strong self-deprecating sense of humour. "And with that in mind, we had better leave this randy stag do and get home. I'm back in Boots at 2pm for the afternoon shift."

The girls packed their things away and headed home back to Hampton Hill High Street, where Anna headed right and into Hampton Hill while Jayne went left and headed off through the housing estate and back to Hampton. Jayne pulled the old black and white photo from her canvas bag and looked at it as she walked.

Who are you? she thought. *And will we ever know?* Letting her mind wander, she wondered what the character of the lady might have been. It may be something she would never know, but that Easter was when strange things started to happen around 39 and 41 Old Road, Hampton, and Jayne would be at the centre of everything that happened.

Good Friday came and went with the normal fish and chips and hot cross buns being the centre of attention for the Church family of 41 Old Road, Hampton. Easter Saturday was a warm one and Bert spent most of his day looking after Uncle Ted's garden which, he had to admit, was looking glorious. Bert put this down to the fact that the police horse had been down Old Road last Wednesday and Bert had been out there with his bucket. As he put it, "The best thing for your rhubarb at this time of the year is a bucket of fresh steaming horse shit."

Mary said that she 'preferred cream on hers'. When he'd finished for the day, he was tired, sweaty and dirty but satisfied that he had kept his promise to his old mate and the garden. He just had a few bedding plants to put in and then that would be that; he would be handing over to the 'new' family that were moving in next week. Fresh blood for the street, he thought, and shivered as the sweat dried on his weary body.

Easter Sunday and real eggs were followed by chocolate eggs. Jayne went out the back door, firstly to let some air in but equally as important, to take in some of that air herself. The Victorian cottage could get stuffy on warm days. She never got any further than opening the door. Laid out on the mat, outside the back entrance, was a trowel, a small hand fork, a pair of gardening gloves, a small rake, pruners and a spray bottle. Jayne shouted back indoors to her dad.

"Dad, why have you left all these tools by the back door?" Bert rose from his breakfast table, leaving the *Mail on Sunday's* sports section behind, and came to see what all the commotion was about.

"What's all the commotion about on my Easter Sunday?" he jovially asked.

Jayne just pointed down at the array of tools, set out like an art exhibition at the Tate Modern. "What are these doing here?" she asked.

"Be buggered if I know. I never left them there." Jayne understood this comment implicitly. Her dad was a stickler for putting everything back exactly as he found it, years of training from her mum. Bert shouted his wife and Mary came to the back-door Easter party.

"What?" she asked. "Why am I here?"

"Did you leave them there?" asked Jayne.

"Why in the name of all that sweet Jesus has blessed us with would I leave a row of tools by the back door? I assume they're yours, Bert. Why are we all stood here like two penneth worth of daft like a scene from that comedy show *The Good Life*?" Jayne was getting slightly exasperated by her parents so took control of the conversation.

"Let's be clear, please. I never put them there and from the looks on your two faces, neither did you. Then who did?"

Bert picked the trowel up and waddled the blade in his hand. It was slightly loose, and the end had been jammed into the handle with a small wedge of wood. "This isn't mine," he said, "this is Ted's." Looking at the rest of the hand tools, Bert confirmed, "They're all Ted's."

"Could a fox have put them there?" asked Mary.

"Only if it's the only fox in the world with opposable thumbs, Mother," answered Jayne, a little unkindly. Bert ignored the two women in his life and picked the tools up. He climbed over the picket fence, his long legs having no problem striding over, and made his way to Ted's shed. The padlock was still locked on the door. He turned to speak but Jayne had pre-empted the question and was already making her way over to him with his keys he was about to ask for.

"Good girl. It's the little red one."

Opening the door, the spaces on the wall from which Ted had attached hooks, screws and nails indicated where each of the tools belonged.

"Well, that's weird," said Bert. 'How in God's name did these get out of here?"

"Are you sure you didn't forget them, Dad, when you finished gardening yesterday?"

"Positive, love. The last thing I do is wash Ted's tools off under the hose and put them back on the wall, just as he always had them. I wouldn't leave it any other way." By now, Mary had walked down her own garden to the gap in the fence and had walked back up Ted's garden to stand with her loved ones at the entrance to the man cave. She caught Jayne's eye and telepathically told her to say nothing, just like mums and daughters all around the world.

"Put them back then, Bert. You must have forgot. Let's not worry about it now. I need you to make some mint sauce for the lamb. Come on, love." The two women walked away back to their own side as Bert placed the tools back on the wall, their outlines etched in dust, like in a young child's game whereby they have to match the coloured shapes to the holes. He was muttering to himself, not happy that his word had been doubted.

The rest of the day went to plan. Jayne went to the cinema in Kingston with Anna that night. They saw *Close*

Encounters of the Third Kind and were both mesmerised by the acting and the unbelievable special effects that realised the spaceship.

Easter Monday morning brought fresh panic to the Church household. Bert was the first up, as he invariably was as soon as the mornings started getting lighter. He had never released himself from the routines he had built into his system during his years in the Royal and Merchant Navies. One of which was up with the light in summer, disregarding his shifts at the council. When he saw the tools on his back door mat again for the second morning running, he knew that someone or something other than his small family was responsible. He left them there until everyone was down for breakfast.

He kept his counsel until the second cup of tea and all the toast had been consumed before leading Mary and Jayne to the back door. He voiced what everyone else was thinking, which for such a practical and straightforward man was not easy.

"Either someone has the key to Ted's shed and is playing a cruel practical joke on us or Ted is letting us know that he hasn't completely gone yet. I'm not too sure of the two options which my preference is."

Jayne remembered the last sentence of his final letter to her: *I'm going to keep in touch, you know.*

"He told us he was going to do this. Remember his letter about keeping in touch," said Jayne.

Mary replied, "I might believe that Ted is talking to us from beyond wherever it is he's gone, but I'm not sure your dad will ever buy it, Jayne."

"No, you're right, Mary, but this is just so strange, isn't it? Who in their right mind would do this for the fun of it? And think about it, who else would have a key? That solicitor fellow. He doesn't strike me as a practical joker. Perhaps Ted is saying to me, 'Take my tools.' Although I can't see that standing up in court should someone accuse me of stealing them."

"Don't be silly, love. They are already yours if you want them. Don't forget his will. It's up to you and me to sort everything out for him in the house. The lawyer is to sell the house, which he's done, and the proceeds are being split everywhere. To his family in Canada, to the forces' charity SSAFA, Battersea Dogs' Home, although the only dog he's ever known is our Penny, and some others that I can't remember. The point is, you can't steal what's already yours."

"I'll have a think about it," said Bert, "I'm not comfortable just taking them. Anyway, we've a lot to do this week before the new family move in, so I'll probably be using them, although the garden's virtually set." The Churches went about their business for the rest of the Bank Holiday Monday and managed to put the thought of being haunted by their old neighbour out of their heads. There were no spooky lights flickering anywhere, rattling of chains or spiritual apparitions to concern them, and so there was no real sense of fear, just one of mystery.

Jayne went out for the day with Anna to Richmond, always a fun place on a sunny bank holiday as long as you don't mind it being busy down by the river. They rented a small engine boat, a 'putt-putt' as Mary called them, and spluttered up and down the Thames, not actually getting that far but having fun shouting back and forth to the other revellers. They all weaved their intricate patterns in and out of each other, like animals in a complicated mating ritual.

Bert finished off the 'bits' he had to do in Ted's garden. Tying some plants back, spot of weeding, one last runaround with the lawnmower, ready for the neighbours at the weekend. Once Ted's garden was virtually perfect, he then moved on to his, but as Mary suggested, he took Ted's tools, which were far better than his own, replacing them in his own shed. Mary was right; effectively, Ted had left his old mucker his tools in his will and so Bert graciously accepted.

Mary did her housework, holiday or no holiday; there were certain chores that had to be completed every day, the box ticked and move on, or Mary simply would not be able to relax for the rest of the day or even sleep that night. She would wipe down every surface in the living room and its adjoining room, in which Susan Holmes would sleep many years later. Then she would quickly run the vacuum around. Monday was always inside-windows day, so using a couple of pages from the *Mail on Sunday* (at last, someone had found something useful for the *Mail*), she would wipe and clean all her inside windows. This ritual went on for a couple of hours until she decided that she would just wipe over Ted's windows as well. She hadn't done them for over a month.

They had lunch and the day had moved on when Mary, armed with scraps of newspaper, a chamois cloth and a bowl, walked past her husband at the bottom of their own garden, through the gap in the fence, built for such moments as this, across Ted's lawn and up to the back door, where she stopped.

"You're not funny, Norbert Church," she shouted over her shoulder to her husband, who was spraying an ants' nest.

Trouble for me if it's my full name, thought Bert. He only ever got Norbert at weddings and funerals and when he was in 'bother with his wife'. He dutifully extricated himself from Ant City and went to see what Mary wanted. He saw her from behind, her cleaning implements discarded on the paved path and her hands firmly on her hips in the internationally recognisable symbol for a pissed-off wife: the dreaded Double Teapot.

"This isn't even remotely funny, Bert," she said, still facing away from him but with her head bent down, looking at something by her feet. Bert, puzzled but nevertheless inquisitive, had to see what Mary was looking at. He peered from behind her like someone wishing to be held back in a fight while shouting, *Let me at him*. There on Ted's back doorstep was a line of garden tools, which Bert immediately recognised.

"They're not Ted's tools. They are mine." Mary looked at him, hearing the incredulity in his voice and knowing her husband well enough to realise he had had nothing to do with the placement of these tools. "And, what's more, I haven't even touched them today. They should still be in our shed."

Mary said what they were both thinking.

"And there's only been us two here. Someone would have had to come through one of the houses or over the fence to get in. Have the right keys, move everything, and get out again without being seen, and one of us has been in the garden all day. We even had our lunch out here."

"Bloody hell, Ted, what are you up to?" questioned Bert.

That evening, the family were all in the front room watching a TV special for Easter Bank Holiday Monday, *ABBA in Switzerland*, so afterwards everyone could remember the time exactly as it started at 7.45pm. Jayne had particularly been looking forward to this as she had been a fan since *Waterloo* and the Eurovision Song Contest win when she was much younger. Plus, guest stars were Roxy Music and Kate Bush, other artists that Jayne 'loved'. Before they heard anything themselves, Penny, the cocker spaniel, started barking, an unusual event in itself as she rarely raised more than a whimper.

"Shh, Penny," said Jayne, trying to enjoy a rendition of *The Name of the Game.* It was just past eight o'clock of the evening. The noise that startled them all came from behind the television, the wall shared with number 39. There was a deep thud, then a series of bangs and at the end an almighty crash.

"Have the new neighbours moved in early?" asked Bert, always looking for the logical answer.

"Should we find out?" asked Mary, straight back at him.

"Well, I'm not coming. I've been looking forward to this programme for weeks since the BBC announced it, and they're just starting *Mamma Mia*," said Jayne.

"Come on then, love, let's get our shoes on and investigate." Mary would never be seen outdoors with her bedroom slippers on. Walking around the front of their house, they entered the small yard in front of number 39 and Bert unlocked the door. Most of the furniture had been removed to a charity, a new home or the 'tip'. The carpets had also been taken up, ready for the new owners. The house smelled of dust, cleaning fluids and death, but only death to those who knew what had happened there, a subliminal odour.

Earlier that month, Bert and Sid, from the pub, had manhandled an old small dark wood wardrobe down the stairs and into the living room. It was to be collected later that week. It had a thin door either side of a central long mirror and a deep bottom drawer. They had left it by the door to the living-room entrance, allowing easy access for the heart charity men. When Mary and Bert entered the living room, the wardrobe was lying flat on its back on the floor on the far side of the room. The marks on the floorboards were fresh and the dust had hardly settled from the movement of the furniture.

"What the hell is happening here?" exclaimed Bert in an accidentally raised voice. He shouted out of surprise and would later admit that he had been frightened, but only to Mary. His wife just stood stock-still with her hand raised to her mouth, like a startled cartoon character from a child's comic. Bert walked over to the fallen wardrobe.

"Be careful, Bert, you don't know what caused this yet. There must be someone else in the house. Come on, let's take a look around." Bert opened the wardrobe doors, thinking that if there was anyone in there, he would be sure to have a heart attack but as he expected, there was just more dust. The couple went from room to room seeing if anything else had been disturbed and after ten minutes of checking around, came to the conclusion that nothing else had moved. Or had been moved. The doors were all locked and all the windows were still closed and latched; the house still retained the old sash windows.

"Nothing else untoward here, Bert," said Mary. "Come on, let's lock up and get back home."

"All right, love. Let's just pick this wardrobe up. I don't like leaving it just lying on the floor like that. If you can help me stand it up, it's not that heavy." Bert moved behind the fallen wardrobe and, taking the top in his hands, he said to his wife, "If I pick it up from the top, you open one of the doors and pull it towards you. I've got the majority of the weight, but you'll just get it upright for me." Bert lifted, Mary pulled and then Mary screamed. In the mirror over her shoulder was the image of a young girl dressed in old-fashioned clothes. The scream made her leave go of the wardrobe, but it was moving quickly enough to right itself with Bert holding the top and side. When Mary unscrewed her eyes and stopped screaming, the image had gone. She looked behind her but there was nothing to see, apart from the doorframe that had housed the image of the young woman.

Mary threw the house keys at Bert and said, "You can lock up, I'm done." She then moved faster than she had for years, giving her knee a sharp rap on the front door as she left. Bert did not know what had gotten into his wife. Muttering to himself, he turned out the lights and shut the front door, ensuring the deadbolt was locked as well.

Mary scooted into her own house and into the living room, collapsing onto her armchair in her position in the room. They always sat in exactly the same positions. ABBA were ironically launching into another of their hits, *Does Your Mother Know*. Jayne could see her mum was upset but still had one eye on the television. Mary was in shock and didn't speak, so Jayne had no option but to address her, ABBA or no ABBA.

"What's up, Mum? You look very pale." Penny had curled up under Mary's feet and was whimpering and shaking.

Mary just shook her head and then said, "Please put the kettle on, Jayne. And get the brandy out from under the stairs." Jayne did as she was asked just as ABBA started their last song, *Thank You For the Music*, which was not one of Jayne's favourites so the least she could do was make her mum a cup of tea, laced liberally with brandy.

The front door slammed and Bert returned, shouting into the kitchen before going into the living room, "Make that two, Jayne. I think we need them."

Moments later, Bert and Mary were sat with hot mugs in their hands and Jayne had turned the television off. The whole event had taken forty minutes and Mary was yet to speak of why she had screamed. Bert, knowing his wife better than he knew himself, waited patiently for her to gather her thoughts, before trying to make sense of what had happened. In the time waiting, he relayed to Jayne the sequence of events leading to the screaming exit of her mum. She wasn't as patient as her dad and so asked, "Come on, Mum, what happened? Why did you run off screaming?"

Mary answered, "Do me a favour, love. Go and get that box that Uncle Ted left you with the money in and letter and everything else that was in there." Jayne looked at her dad and shrugged her shoulders, before charging upstairs to her room and returning with the tin box that Ted had kept hidden in his hearth. She handed the box to her mum.

"Can I open this, Jayne?"

"Of course you can, Mum. You don't need to ask." Carefully opening the lid, as though it contained a live World War II hand grenade, she rummaged under the remaining money and the letter until she got to what she was looking for. She held the photograph up in front of her and gasped. A single tear slid down her cheek.

"That's her. I saw her tonight. She's the lady in the mirror. In Ted's house, in the wardrobe. That's her, I swear it is. Just for a second, she was there. Looking just like this. Except she wasn't smiling." The emotions became overwhelming for Mary, and she began to sob until her shoulders shook.

"Come on, love, don't be like this." Bert struggled to deal with a crying woman even if it was his wife of decades gone. "Tell us exactly what happened." Mary sipped her brandy tea and then told Bert and Jayne exactly what had happened.

"I can see you're shocked, Mum, but why are you crying so hard?"

"I'm not sure, love. I guess it's the shock. I've never seen a ghost before."

"You've not seen a ghost, Mum. You're just tired. You've

been working on Ted's house and wondering who the girl in the picture is and thinking of Ted and who he was to her. Then the wardrobe falling over and Dad's tools and everything and it's just become too much for you. That's all, you haven't seen a ghost."

"Whatever you think, Jayne, but you weren't there. Trust me. I know what I saw, and it wasn't exactly like the photo you have of her either. She looked at me just for a second, and I felt it, I felt how she felt. She was so, so sad." Mary started to cry again, and it was several hours before she could get it out of her head and get a few hours' sleep.

Earlier that day, 220 miles away in St Helens, a well-attended funeral was held for Elsie Tremaine. A lady who had lived the majority of her life in the town of her birth.

Old Road, Hampton

2007

A Journal

August 7th

Tuesday – OMG! Jayne has told me the whole story about Uncle Ted and Mary and Bert and the lady in the photo. I've looked at the photo, isn't she beautiful! That must be Ted's long-lost love that went wrong, don't you think, journal? And Mary saw her in the mirror of Uncle Ted's wardrobe. She must have been in that house with him and come back to say goodbye. I think I'm making it romantic so that it doesn't scare me anymore.

What about Bert's tools going over to number 39 and Uncle Ted's tools landing up at the back door? I thought I heard a little boy's voice, but it could have been a woman's, I guess. 'Susan', is what I heard, my name. How could they know my name? I've spoken to Mary on the phone and struck up quite a friendship with her even though there must be fifty-five years between us. Even to this day she is adamant that she saw something in the mirror and 'wasn't just seeing things'. To be fair, I'm utterly convinced I heard a ball bouncing next to me and, let's be honest, it isn't the normal noise you would associate with a ghost or an apparition. Not if you believe Hollywood and Stephen King.

One thing is for sure: I'm never sleeping in that back room again. Luckily, weekend just gone, Julie, she's my older sister if you've forgotten, went back to Basingstoke. Jayne told me another couple of occasions when they thought Uncle Ted or 'The Lady in the Mirror' made their presence known again.

Firstly, a couple of days after 'Wardrobegate' or as Dad calls it, 'Wardrobedoor', Bert was in the garden where the two gardens met up at the back. The two gardens run parallel to each other about 100 and 20 foot long but quite narrow. In those days, a picket fence ran down the middle but only halfway down. The bottom part was almost communal between Bert and Uncle Ted. When he died in 1978, he left the bottom part of his garden to Bert and Mary in his will. So, Jayne and her mum and dad got a long garden that opened up into a bowl at the bottom, really rare to get so much space in this part of London.

Sorry for all the back story, but Bert had built a bonfire in the communal bit of the garden to burn off some garden refuse and some bits and pieces from Ted's. It was just before the new people were moving in and Bert and Mary wanted everything to be lovely for them. I think they're a good example of the dying breed of British neighbourhood community that lasted through the '50s and '60s and some of the '70s but started to fall away, especially today in 2007.

Perhaps I'm being too cynical, but that generation seemed to go out of their way to help each other compared to now.

He had Penny with him, which Jayne said was her spaniel. I've seen a photo of her, a beautiful tan and white cocker with chestnut brown eyes straight out of *Lady and the Tramp*. Anyway, as Bert threw some of Ted's old things onto the bonfire (regulations being somewhat lax in the 1970s), a wind blew through, according to Bert, and the fire flamed high. Penny crouched down in the grass, head on her paws, snuffling and pawing at the grass. Then she started shaking, before jumping up and bolting up the garden and through the house, where they found her nestled up amongst the old shoes under the stairs.

Apparently, it took them a long time to coax her out. This had never happened before and would never happen again.

Eventually, the new family moved in next door. Mum, Dad and baby. Jayne doesn't remember their names as she was away at college for most of the time they lived there. Mary said the family name was Connor and thinks they were Sharon, Mike, and the baby was Jack. Years later, I think every boy born in the 2000s was called Jack; I know more Jacks than any other name. They were only there six months, no word of a lie.

One day, Sharon asked Mary if anything had happened in the back room facing the garden, as she always felt cold in there. She said Jack would never settle in that room and some nights wouldn't settle anywhere in the house, but in my opinion that's the same for most babies. Mary obviously told her that was the room that Uncle Ted had died in. But they moved out. Didn't like the house. Didn't like the room, and

Sharon told Mary that she just never felt comfortable. After that, the Sharrocks moved in, and they are still there today.

That was the last of the strange incidents. Mary and Bert, more so Mary, are convinced that Uncle Ted was restless after he died. He had a message that he wanted to tell Jayne, it seems, and then there's the photograph. Of whom, we still have no idea. You would think in this day and age we would be able to find out, but records weren't as good when this photo was taken.

So, we have three people: Uncle Ted, the Lady in the Mirror and the child (or lady) bouncing the ball. Are they all linked? Or are they three completely unrelated incidents that with a scientific investigation team would be completely explainable? Believe what you will, journal, but I'm still not sleeping downstairs on my own.

On a lighter note, I don't think I'm going to be able to hack this job. I'm bored out my skull. Alan, my older brother, did a course to teach English as a foreign language and suggested I should do the same. Do you know what? I think I will.

Christleton, Cheshire

2019

It was a beautiful spring Saturday morning in Christleton, and Anne and Colin Smith were taking a stroll around the village. Colin was working from home this coming week so Anne would be able to spend some quality time with her husband, who for once had a quiet April in terms of business travel. They made an unusual-looking couple; her tall, slim, stork-like physique at odds with Colin's middle-aged but broad-shouldered gym-bulked body. Their daughters said they looked like an elf and a Uruk-hai out for a stroll, which was a little unkind but always made them laugh.

They walked up Little Heath Road past the Methodist church around the duck pond, over to the cricket club and playing fields and then back to the road. It was a little over a mile round trip so depending on the weather and mood they would keep going until they felt fully exercised. On a day like today it was a pleasure to be alive, and the greetings from the wildfowl, as they passed alongside the pond, filled their hearts and heads with a sense of wellbeing.

Anne was telling Colin about the results from her DNA test.

"A lot of it doesn't make a great deal of sense to me, to be honest, Col. Actually, I don't mean that. What I mean is, it doesn't exactly tell me anything. Here, look at this printout." She showed him two pie charts headed up 'You' and then the second was 'Parent 1' fifty per cent and 'Parent 2' another fifty per cent.

"So, this is me. I'm forty-five per cent England and north-western Europe; twenty-two per cent Irish; twenty per cent from Scotland; six per cent Germanic Europe; five per cent from Norway and two per cent Sweden and Denmark. From that, they then estimate what your parents could have been, but it doesn't tell you who is Dad and who is Mum. They would have to do their own DNA tests for that and obviously for Dad, that won't ever happen now."

Colin took a brief look.

"From my perspective, after nearly three years, at least you've used the present I bought you. But I do see what you mean. Not really what you're looking for, is it?"

Anne responded. "Well, to be honest, I'm not sure what I am looking for. Clarity, I guess. But what they also do is match you up on their database with other people who have such a close match to your DNA that they could potentially be related to you. I quickly read another email before we left today."

Colin laughed and said, "Is this when you find out that Jack the Ripper is your great- grandad or something?"

"Well, I'm hoping for something a little more wholesome myself. They match you to people who are still alive and then you get in touch with them and try and merge the family trees if they do merge. If not, you just move on. It's not easy for me as I have a large gap just two generations away so it's more of a treasure hunt. I just hope the treasure chest hasn't already been raided by the time I find it. It is exciting, though. It would be nice to finally know who exactly I am."

Colin leant over and kissed his wife.

"I know who you are. You're the wonderful mum of two great girls, a fantastic wife whose stupid husband leaves her on her own too much and a primary school teacher that is loved by everyone she ever teaches. Anne Smith, that's who you are."

"They are some of the nicest words you've ever used about me. What have you done?" She laughed, quite loudly, and that set the ducks off on the pond and they volleyed her laugh back with interest, so the air was filled with a cacophony of quacks and wings splashing the water as they became agitated. She linked her arm through Colin's and said, "Come on, let's go and get a coffee and perhaps a spot of brunch at the Cheshire Cat. We can discuss this more because I have an idea that I may want to pursue, and I want to know what you think." The pub was about a twenty-minute walk from the pond, and they had worked up a healthy appetite by the time they got there. Anne went for the buttermilk pancakes with pancetta and maple syrup, while Colin took the eggs benedict on a toasted muffin with pulled ham and hollandaise. They shared a cafetiere of hot Brazilian coffee, both black with no sugar.

"How coffee was always meant to be drunk," said Colin, not knowing or caring if what he said was true or not. "So, now you've finished your food, what's this email you want to show me?" Anne tapped out on her iPhone and then passed it over to her husband. They were silent while Colin read and took in the life-changing message captured on the technology in his hand. He looked up at his wife.

"Okay then. You think this may be a true lead? Someone who may be related to you in some way or form?" Anne was deadly serious and just nodded her assent.

"What would you like to do about it? Have you contacted her yet?"

Anne at last got her voice back.

"I only received the email this morning, but the onus is now on one of us to contact the other. I suppose it depends how serious this lady is. All I have is an email address, not even a name yet. We are matched purely on the strands of DNA that make up our unique blueprint for life. The reason I'm talking to you is if she wants to pursue the connection, I want to meet her."

"If she wants to meet you?" asked Colin.

"Yes, of course this only works if both sides are agreeable, but I think she is. Otherwise, why go on the website in the first place and look for matches and, secondly, she has already sent me a brief note. It just says hello, nice to meet you, etc., etc. But there was an attachment, a file. Pass my phone. I believe this is her."

Anne found the email and opened the attachment. It was a photo. She passed her phone back to Colin. Colin gasped.

"It's you," he said, "you, ten or fifteen years ago. Same smile, blonde hair, high cheekbones and most strikingly the same diamond blue eyes. I agree you must meet up with this lady."

"There is a slight issue with that, Col. Have you seen her email? It ends with .ca and do you know where that is?" Colin looked back up, still mesmerised by the resemblance between the photograph and the woman sat opposite him at the table.

They both spoke at the same time.

"Canada!"

St Helens, Merseyside

1975

"Am I adopted, Dad?" James Holmes, known to his National Service colleagues as Rocky, a name which had long been abandoned by everyone apart from one of James's drinking mates who never called him anything but Rocky, walked through his back door clutching a bag of Pimbletts pies and a couple of bread rolls for his and his son's dinner, and was greeted with this question. He could see that his son Graham, known to his friends as Locky, nicknamed after the great detective Sherlock Holmes, was waving an old document in his hands. One that he had seen and read many, many times over the preceding years.

"You haven't got the soup ready," he answered. "You know I only get forty-five minutes for lunch. By the time I've walked to the car, driven here and back, it doesn't leave much time for us to eat our dinners." In the north-west of England, your three meals a day chronologically were breakfast, dinner and tea. Later on in life, Graham would be surprised when he moved south to find that they were called breakfast, lunch and dinner.

He placed the bag of food carefully on the kitchen table as though handling something far more precious than two pies and two bread rolls. Graham was still stood brandishing the newly found documentation above his head as though he had just written a declaration of independence for a third-world country. His dad grabbed a tin of Heinz chicken broth from the cupboard and took the can opener from the drawer.

"Butter the bread for me, please, son, and put the pies on the plates. If we're quick enough, they should still be warm." Graham's mind was whirling but so was his father's. James Holmes had known that this day would come but was not ready for the conversation just now. He was a civil servant working in local government offices and knew full well he had to be back at his desk on time or face the consequences. And yet he also knew that this was a very important conversation that he had to have with his eldest son.

Graham put down what he knew to be adoption papers of some description but didn't understand the names on them. The two worked around each other like a clockwork toy that had just been wound; everything in synchronisation. They had danced the lunchtime kitchen tango together many times and even though both their minds were far from the mundane tasks of pulling their 'dinner' together, their dance training stood them in good stead. James had the soup on the electric hotplate, bowls already next to him ready to receive their offering as he stirred, making sure the soup didn't stick to the bottom of the pan. Graham, holding onto his dance partner's shoulders as he whirled him around the kitchen, had the pies on plates, the bread board out and was applying thick slathers of margarine to the rolls even though they still called it 'buttering the bread'.

Moments later, they were both sat on the breakfast benches facing each other over their hot soup bowls. Graham looked at his dad and, without speaking, pointed to the papers he had found earlier 'under the stairs'.

"Come on, Dad, what does this all mean? I'm actually scared now."

"There's nothing for you to worry about or be scared about. It's not about you, it's about me. I was going to tell you when you turned eighteen but as you've found out anyway."

"I've not found out owt yet. I don't know what it all means," answered Graham. The dance had moved from the kitchen floor to the kitchen table as they ate their soup, rolls and pies, taking mouthfuls between words in time to some unheard tune.

James sighed heavily and said, "I need a little time to think about how to tell you this, son, but the papers are my papers. You are not adopted, don't worry. Me and your mum are your mum and dad. That's that. There's no mystery, but I do need to tell you my story. I don't have time but tonight when I get in from work, I promise I'll tell you everything. Is that okay?"

Graham shrugged as though he'd been asked to tidy his room and had unwillingly assented.

"It'll have to be, I guess. Is there anything to worry about?"

"I swear to you, there is absolutely nothing to worry about. I just want to tell it properly and don't have time." James then seemed to get a little annoyed.

"What the bloody hell was you doing rooting under the stairs for anyway? You must have seen these were important documents, not for you?"

"I was looking for me old boots. I was just going for a kickaround." Graham then remembered what had happened to them first thing that morning. It seemed a lifetime ago.

"Anyway, a man flashed his willy at us all this morning in the woods and we all had to run off. Charlie and Mush's mum sent me home because we couldn't stop laughing." James Holmes was thinking about all his worst days coming at once.

"Jesus, some blokes. Well, don't go back there, whatever you do. Wait for me or your mum to get home later. Then we can have a talk about these papers, and you can tell us about what happened in the woods. Do me a favour. Don't mention any of this to Anne or David, please. They're not old enough to understand yet. You're grown up enough now to be able to keep a secret. It's only a white lie and not even that as you're not going to be asked about anything."

"What's the secret, the willy man or this?" Graham held aloft the offending document.

"For the time being, both," answered his dad. "But your sister and brother will need to know about the woods at some point to keep them safe. And don't call him the willy man."

"We called him much worse in the woods earlier."

"Who was with you, just you, Charlie and Mush?"

"No, there was the Dobeys as well and Faz and Inchy."

"Well, at least there's some safety in numbers, I suppose. I have to go now. Do the dishes so your mum doesn't get home from work to a dirty kitchen, and we'll have a talk."

Later that evening, Graham found out a few stories from his dad's National Service in 1959.

Hong Kong

1959

The three *caballeros* had made it to Hong Kong and mostly in one piece: or to be accurate three pieces. Ginger had lost his kit and a large chunk of his pride in Colombo; Jock had ended up with food poisoning from Singapore; and Rocky, well, he had received one punishment of jankers for being late waiting for a mate, which he never did again, but generally his reputation had been enhanced somewhat by his all-round knowledge of the world through the mystical, magical medium of picking a book up occasionally and reading it. Or even a newspaper for anything other than the horse racing form and yesterday's results.

They were due to spend eight or nine months in Hong Kong, which would take them through to May/June 1960.

They had packed their duffle bags that morning and were waiting on deck with the hundreds of other squaddies. This was what all the training was for and the men simply couldn't contain their excitement. Away from home in an exotic setting with many new friends and the sense of camaraderie that the British Forces instil in its troops, the men were simply wild animals, once held in captivity, being released back to the wild.

"This is it, lads. Stick close by, you two, and we'll try and get the same posting."

"Who put you in charge, Rocky?" asked the red man mountain that was Ginger.

"Okay then, what do you suggest, Ginger?" replied Rocky.

"Let's stick together and see if we can get the same posting." Ginger winked at Rocky, laughed, and all was good. The sergeant lined them all up and gave some speech about being British and representing the queen and the Lancaster Brigade but no one was listening. All their attention was on the mayhem that was Hong Kong Harbour in 1959. There were people and boats everywhere. Tiny little fishing boats with room for one or two men at most dotted the whole harbour like breadcrumbs on a pond. They vied for space with mid-size cruisers and traditional motor boats, who themselves were trying to keep out of the way of the full-size warships, such as the *Empire Fowey* had once been. The squaddies looked but they had little time to take in their surroundings as out on the pier were a gang of troop carrier army trucks that they were loaded onto and whisked away before the young Hong Kong market sellers had taken their chance to say, "Present for girlfriend," while holding up some dubious bottles of proposed perfumes.

They were on their way to Stanley Barracks, where they were sorted into different companies. Ginger, Rocky and Jock managed to get seconded to the motor lot, which suited Rocky perfectly as he was hoping to become a driver.

Corporal Tyldesley lined up his new recruits and asked if he had any drivers. Three men stepped forward; James Rocky Holmes was one of them. He in fact had never driven a car in his life but was the proud owner of a Triumph Tigercub motorbike back home so had driven a bike on hundreds of occasions. He hoped that would prove useful, especially as the Corporal wanted three drivers and only had three volunteers, including himself.

Jock whispered to him out of the side of his mouth – he wouldn't have made a very good spy, would Jock – "Psst, Rocky. You never said you could drive."

"Psst. Well, you never asked," he answered. "Say nowt, I'm bluffing."

They were all dismissed and sent to their barracks to unpack and get their bearings. Later that day, the three erstwhile drivers were sent for and quick marched down from the top floor of the barracks via the metal stairs attached to one end of the two-storey building. Their mess was below them so during the day the smells of cooking food would rise up to the soldiers, leaving them ravenous before their meals were served. As Ginger said, "Why does it always smell like the Ritz but taste like Pedigree Chum?"

Corporal Tyldesley lined up his three young drivers in front of three one-ton army trucks known as 'onetunners', with no gap between the one and the tunner! They were stood on the parade ground with a road marked out with plastic cones. Rocky knew how a car worked and actually knew how to drive one, but only in his head. Now he was about to be let loose on the twisty, windy, narrow roads of Hong Kong in a onetunner.

Bloody hell, he thought, *have I gone too far this time? These look massive.* They were in fact Austin light trucks, but one ton was considered light for an army truck. One thing was for sure; it was a lot bigger and heavier than Rocky's Triumph Tigercub.

"Names?" asked the Corporal. "And I like to be called sir," he stressed.

"Holmes, sir," answered Rocky, closely followed by

"Macrae, sir," and

"Rooney, sir."

"Have any of you driven anything as big as these before?" Rooney answered.

"Yes, sir. I drove bigger than these in my civilian job, sir."

"Did I ask for your fucking life story, Private Rooney? Get in and drive around those cones down there. You'll see there's a trailer attached to the back of the trucks, so I want to see you drive forwards around the cones. Then do the same in reverse and then reverse park back where you found it. Understand, Private Rooney?"

"Sir," was all Rooney said this time.

"Well, get on with it then, man." Rooney broke ranks and ran quickly over to the truck. Pulling himself up into the cab, he frantically looked for the ignition. Upon finding it, he saw there was no key in it. Sweating now, 35 degrees and humid, he gazed through droplets of perspiration and a misting windscreen. Corporal Tyldesley was dangling a key from his thumb and first finger. He was clearly enjoying himself at the expense of the three new squaddies. Rocky distinctly heard Rooney utter that well-known prayer of anxiety.

"Shit," said Rooney.

"Missing something, Private?"

"Sir." Rooney started to get down from the cab before the Corporal, his fun now over, said, "Stay there. I'm getting in next to you. You don't think the army will let someone who's only ever driven a milk float before loose on the roads of Hong Kong in one of our expensive trucks, do you, Private?"

"No, sir," answered the rapidly becoming bewildered young soldier, now wishing he'd never stepped forward when asked if there were any drivers.

Corporal I***** C***** – "So, in general, here's the youth of the country, dissipating their energies in utterly non-productive wasted activity, while the country, badly needing their labour, moulders and stagnates."

Corporal Tyldesley jumped up into the passenger seat of the onetunner and issued the brief but accurate instructions.

"Drive past the cones at the bottom of the parade ground. Then stop and reverse back and park back here. Now."

Private Rooney started the engine, leaving the key turned too long so that the engine whirred like a strangled animal. He put the clutch in and stalled. Rooney started the engine again, once more whirring, but he'd left the truck in first gear. He stalled again. Corporal Tyldesley screamed an obscenity. Rooney this time kept his foot on the clutch, wondering if it was actually possible to shove the key where the Corporal had just suggested it would be going if he didn't.

Rocky and Macrae stole a glance at each other. Their sympathy very much rested with their colleague, but Rocky was wondering if claiming he could drive was such a clever idea now. Nevertheless, he genuinely believed he would be a better driver than the beleaguered Rooney. The truck was jerking its way down the parade ground by now with the Corporal offering words of encouragement such as, "What will your wife say, Rooney, when you return home without your bollocks?" Or the ever-popular, "Did your mother know they kept the afterbirth and threw the baby away?" The problem Rooney was having was that he had never driven a truck before that didn't have synchronisers and therefore he had to double declutch. What this effectively meant was (double declutching really is what it says on the tin), for one gear change, you push the clutch in twice. Once to move out of gear and into neutral, and again to move into your chosen gear. But this alone won't get your engine, clutch, gearbox and driveshaft as in sync as a marching band.

Let's use an example. Say you want to shift from fourth to third; you'll come off the power, dip the clutch, move the gearstick to neutral and let the clutch back up. Then you'll use the throttle so that revs match road speed, then dip the clutch again, select third gear and let the clutch out.

No one had ever explained this process to Private Rooney, and the screaming obscenities flying in his direction coupled with a small proportion of spittle were not going to facilitate a 'Eureka' moment for him. Rooney girded his loins and through sheer persistence and a good common-sense understanding of cars and their engines eventually worked out the gear changes. He completed the procedure only for the Corporal to shout loudly in his ear, "Again, but this time without farting up and down the parade square." The second time was a little better and the third time, one could say, was fart free.

"Back to your barracks, Rooney. This is your vehicle now. You will look after it as well as you look after your rifle. No one else will touch your vehicle. It is yours and yours alone. You are totally responsible for it. When we have finished here, you will house it in garage number twelve. That's it, dismissed." The Corporal threw the keys to Rooney, which he caught, then saluted and double marched off the square as quickly as he could. His retelling of the story later in the mess would paint him as something more of a hero than he actually had been, but such is the telling of tales.

"Macrae. Second truck. Keys are in the ignition. Same routine. Now you know it double declutches, so I expect better from you, or you'll be eating mouldy bread for a week."

"Sir," shouted back Macrae. To his major credit, Macrae, who did drive a lorry in the civilian world, did not let the shouting Corporal Tyldesley interrupt his concentration and his real-life training shone through, giving the non-commissioned officer little to get hot under the collar about. As if the heat in Hong Kong wasn't enough to stop him charging about speaking at ten times the volume of anybody else. Macrae only had to drive two circuits and the Corporal re-issued his final orders again.

"Back to your barracks, Macrae. This is your vehicle now. You will look after it as well as you look after your rifle. No one else will touch your vehicle. It is yours and yours alone. You are totally responsible for it. When we have finished here, you will house it in garage number thirteen. That's it, dismissed."

Rocky did think, *At least he's consistent.*

Rocky was the last man standing, alone with his nemesis. He understood engines through his motorbike and while having never before driven a car, never mind a one-ton truck, understood the concepts of gears, revolutions, synchronisers, the biting point and other such creative mechanical engine terms. Corporal Tyldesley was at his own biting point.

"Get in, Holmes. You know the drill now." A crowd had gathered on the upstairs barrack balconies and many of Rocky's squaddie mates had heard the commotion created initially by Rooney and numbers had gathered.

"Sir," replied Rocky Holmes. He understood the concept of double declutching but now he prepared to take his first-ever practical test of his book knowledge. Rocky had the advantage of seeing where his fellow trainee drivers had gone wrong. He started the engine, leaving the key the second the engine engaged. Straight into first and away the truck rolled. Clutch, out of first, disengage clutch, clutch again, into second, re-engage. The truck picked up speed smoothly. Same procedure for third before having to slow down as he reached the end of the parade ground.

He found reverse and, looking back over his left shoulder, manoeuvred the truck backwards from whence it came. He stopped perfectly, not in exactly the same parked position but close enough for government work. He dared a smile.

"Take that fucking grin off your face before I wipe it off with a shithouse mop."

"Yes, sir," answered a startled Rocky. He could hear his mates chanting from the balcony. Both got out of the truck at the Corporal's signal and Rocky received his last orders.

"Back to your barracks, Holmes. This is your vehicle now.

You will look after it as well as you look after your rifle. No one else will touch your vehicle. It is yours and yours alone. You are totally responsible for it. When we have finished here, you will house it in garage number fourteen. That's it, dismissed."

Rocky saluted and turned to go, but the Corporal asked one more question.

"Holmes, why was everyone chanting Rocky?"

"Sir, because it's my nickname, sir. I'm called it because I look like I've just crawled from under a rock, sir."

Even Corporal Tyldesley couldn't stop himself from smiling and then laughing at that comment. Rocky seized his moment.

"Sir, permission to speak, sir."

"Go ahead, Holmes."

"Sir, I don't have a driving licence, sir."

"Please tell me this is not true, Holmes. You were the best bloody driver of the three. Why in the name of sweet Jesus Christ would you waste my time? You are on jankers for three months if this is true."

"Sir, permission to speak again, sir." The Corporal just glared at Rocky and if looks could indeed kill then Rocky would have been something resembling a piece of burnt toast, such was the intensity of the look.

"Go on and make it good."

"Sir, I've driven many a time back home. I just never got around to passing the test. I drive a motorbike, sir, and I understand engines and how they work. I'm sure I would pass the test here in ten minutes, sir, if I were given the chance. Sir." Corporal Tyldesley wiped a hand over his reddening face. Rocky thought that the Corp may have a heart attack if he didn't calm down. For the record, Rocky was twenty-two years old, after turning so on board ship. The Corporal was the grand old age of twenty-seven so unless he was hiding a major genetic disorder wouldn't be having a heart attack anytime soon.

"Get back behind the wheel."

"Sir?"

"Get back in the fucking truck. I'll test you now. If you fail, I swear by all that's fucking holy you will have the worst twelve months of your disgusting little life here in Hong Kong."

"Sir." Rocky was back up in the cab quicker than his bride's nightie had been up on their wedding night. Tyldesley sat next to him.

"Drive to the end of the parade ground, take a left and then an immediate right back down the mountain. Do not forget you have a twelve-foot trailer strapped to the back. I hope I don't regret this, Holmes." Rocky pulled away, double declutching for all he was worth. His mates on the balcony had no clue what was happening but gave him a cheer for luck anyway. The left turn was no problem; the right was almost a U-turn and Rocky slowed right down, sweat dripping into his eyes as he had inches to spare on either side. He was in no danger as the truck was hemmed in with walls, but he knew if he hit one, he could expect a tough tour of duty. He didn't know how tough.

The trailer behind him was going to scrape right along the wall and so Rocky, now in the moment, stopped. He slipped the one-ton truck into neutral and then into reverse, thus creating a better angle for swinging the entire length around the corner. He did so without a touch.

Even Corporal Tyldesley was impressed, although only his mother could have known from the straight poker face. Rocky picked up speed again and was soon rolling the truck down the narrow mountainous road. It was something of a workout, swinging the truck back and forth until reaching the flat of the bottom.

"Swing it around and put it in neutral, Holmes," said the Corporal. "Final test, a hill start." Rocky parked up the onetunner and thought if this was a hill start, he wouldn't like to do a mountain one. The slope in front of him was at least a 'one in three', which meant for every three yards forward the gradient went up one yard. This was not going to be easy, especially with so much weight on the back in the form of the trailer. Rocky crunched it into gear, held the clutch as close to biting point as possible and slowly released the hand brake. There was a tremor, but no roll backwards, and Rocky took the truck back up the mountain at a much slower pace than the downward trip. And then it happened.

Rocky wasn't by any means speeding but when the dog ran into the road he wouldn't stop in time, and he couldn't get all the way past the dog because of the length of the rig. Either side of him were built-up concrete buildings with plain white walls but there was nowhere to go. The dog had run out of a doorway that Rocky later admitted he had never seen. The dog ran straight across him and wedged itself against the far wall. Rocky hit the brakes and swung the wheel hard towards the whimpering animal but getting the front part of the truck past the dog.

He then deliberately jackknifed the truck and trailer, creating a wedge shape around the dog and bringing them to a complete stop. A child chased the mongrel, ran under the truck, picked it up and ran back into the doorway. The whole event had taken no more than ten seconds. *That's me finished*, thought Rocky.

The Corporal was as shook up as Rocky but motioned for him to start the engine and get going again. They arrived back on the parade ground ten minutes later after a very careful return to the barracks. No one had spoken since the near accident. The Corporal jumped from the cab like a cork from a bottle and popped onto the parade ground. Rocky Holmes did the same and stood to attention in front of him.

Corporal Tyldesley said, "Back to your barracks, Holmes. This is your vehicle now. You will look after it as well as you look after your rifle. No one else will touch your vehicle. It is yours and yours alone. You are totally responsible for it. When we have finished here, you will house it in garage number fourteen. You have passed your test and I'll see to it that the paperwork is completed properly as when you get back to civilian life the licence is valid. That's it, dismissed."

"Sir, thank you, sir," intoned Rocky.

"One more thing, Holmes. If you tell anyone this, I will deny it and put you on jankers for a month, but that was the best piece of instinctive driving I have ever seen. Dismissed."

Rocky saluted one more time and double marched back to his barracks.

The next few months were good ones for Rocky, Ginger and Jock, and they really started to enjoy their National Service time. Rocky spent most of his days driving around Hong Kong with the Corporal at his side. It seemed he had taken quite a shine to Rocky, especially as he had selected him without a driving licence and then passed him. Rocky used the expression, 'If I could pass my test there, I could pass it anywhere', for the rest of his life.

His wife, Lizzie, used the expression, 'At least he got something out of the army'.

Rocky and his mates were the lucky ones as for every man who was either suited to the life or managed to enjoy it, there was one who absolutely hated it and found the strict daily and weekly routines difficult to cope with.

Private T***** B*****, Royal Sussex Regiment – "I made comrades the like of which I have never done again. I looked forward to demob for two years but when the day came, 'Christ, hey, I'm going to miss you guys.'"

Private J***** V******** – "Private Smith said to me while we waited, 'Joe,' he said, 'when people ask you what National Service was like, don't forget to tell them it was awful. It was fuckin' awful,' he said. I have never forgotten that chap's words."

During 1959, the British Motor Corporation, BMC, manufactured and released the new Morris Mini Minor, forever known as the 'Mini'. The first 300 manufactured at Cowley in Oxford were mainly for export; only twenty-six were retained in the United Kingdom. Ginger, Rocky, Jock and the other troops at the Stanley Barracks in Hong

Kong were blessed that late autumn as a Chinese car dealer imported half a dozen new Minis and as a marketing ploy took them to the parade ground at the barracks.

The squaddies not on duty 'legged' it down to the parade ground to take a look, and many of them took the opportunity of driving one. Rocky, an official driver, was one of the first to take a spin. Window wound down, arm leaning on the door, Ginger by his side (so not the perfect scenario), his head touching the roof of the car he was so big, Rocky took the new Mini through its paces. As his mates looked on in admiration, he shouted, "It's like driving a bloody Rolls-Royce after those bleeding trucks."

Three years later, Rocky would own his own Mini but not quite of the same quality as the one he drove in Hong Kong. On the car he could afford back home, he only managed to keep his number plate attached with a strip of coat hanger wire. The previous driver had not been as careful as Rocky and had been involved in a couple of alcohol-fuelled prangs, leaving the number plate in a sorry state.

On their days off, the men would jump onto the *Star Ferry* that ran between Hong Kong Victoria Island and the mainland. It was worth ten cents of any soldier's money and ran twenty-four seven, proving a useful mode of transport for many a squaddie trying to get back to camp at an unsociable hour. Rocky, Ginger and Jock once went all the way up to the Chinese border, not the most thoughtful of moves, wearing their British uniforms. The shouts and pointing of machine guns from the battlements did not get lost in translation and they quickly removed themselves from possible danger. The soldiers were, for very good reason, not allowed across the border but did undertake training on the mainland, but that was as close as the British Army got to China.

They spent their money on wine, women and song and wasted the rest (as Ginger used to say). But prices were such that Rocky always managed to send money home as he and Lizzie were saving for their first house. Shirts were five Hong Kong dollars, the equivalent of five shillings threepence, and for an extra dollar you could have it made to measure. In the UK at the time a shirt would have cost Rocky one pound ten shillings, so Rocky could buy five made-to-measure shirts for the price of one off the shelf back home, and still have change for a couple of pints.

Life was good. Ginger became the strong man of the camp, taking on all comers at digging a trench. One of the drills was digging yourself a trench deep enough to crouch in to provide cover to shoot from. Rocky was still on his third shovelful of dirt while Ginger was already sat in his hole waiting for him.

"If we go into battle, I'm with Ginger," said Jock, soon chorused by all within earshot. There was even a little church on camp that was frequented by about twenty lads from the regiment as well as officers and their wives. Rocky was leaving after Sunday service with Jock (Ginger had suggested they shove religion up their arses, taken from the Gospel of Saint Paul apparently) and several others of their colleagues. Only one of them was carrying a prayer book; the rest just sauntered out, lighting up their cigarettes as they hit the fresh air.

Afterwards, Rocky described it as reminiscent of Jesus throwing the money lenders from the temple. The priest, or chaplain, stopped the men en masse and 'roasted' them for only having one prayer book amongst so many men. Fire and brimstone rained down on them in the only true action any of them would experience. Rocky was not the owner of the prayer book so took the tongue-lashing from the chaplain, head down, penitent. Afterwards, they all decided if that was 'Catholicism' then Ginger had been correct. They could stick it where the sun didn't shine. This was interesting for Rocky as when he was a child he never missed Catholic mass on a Sunday and was raised as a strong Catholic.

So strong in fact that his own brother Frank was about to declare to the family that his intention was to head out on the journey of becoming a Catholic priest. Rocky would read this news just after Christmas in a letter from Frank, the letter that would change his life. Rocky took his mail from the guard and went outside to sit in the shade underneath the outside stairway that led up to the mess. He sat with his back against the wall, the shadow of the staircase leading out into the parade ground like a stairway that led to nowhere. Sat under the stairs, Rocky read his news.

A Letter from Frank Holmes

1959

6 Harris Avenue,
West Park,
St Helens,
Lancashire,
England.
27th November 1959

Dear James,

It's Frank here. Hope you're having a good time in Hong Kong. It's November here now and I don't know when you'll get this but it's blowing a gale most nights. May and Ken send their love. Well, May did. I can't write what Ken actually said as the authorities might stop the letter.

Jim Sullivan has finished at Saints and Alan Prescott has taken over. We got beat in the Lancashire Cup Final 5-4 by Warrington. Bloody hard game, you'd have loved it. The

Aussies are still touring. They beat us at Knowsley Road 15-2 and it's one-all at the moment in the test matches, with the last one in December. We're going well in the league, only lost one, and as I write this we're top.

I know you don't expect me to write but I've been having a think about my life and wanted to tell you a couple of things, especially as you're married now, and all grown up and that. After the war and my further stint in the navy, when I went back to Pilks, I never felt comfortable. I felt a bit lost. I saw some things that we're just not supposed to see, and it's changed my outlook on stuff.

Don't get me wrong. I work hard like I always have and still enjoy a pint in the Windle and a trip to Saints, especially the big games like Wigan or a test match. But, James, I saw so much hate and anger and cruelty that I want to do something about it. So, to get to it, I've enrolled to be a priest, a Catholic priest. As you might imagine, May is delighted. She thinks God himself has come down into Harris Avenue and blessed the Holmes family. Our May's Fred couldn't care less, simply doesn't believe nor ever will.

I think I can do some good, James. I'm not a stupid man and I've lived as a man even though I've never been married. I've had girlfriends and I've been to war, so I know what I'm going to miss, but it's a sacrifice worth taking, I believe. I want to work in some of the deprived areas around where we live, not necessarily St Helens but the north-west. There are so many families still on the breadline and I think my life experience will be helpful to others.

This is going to sound daft to you, but you know in the Bible when it says someone's speaking to God or 'Saul' heard the call of God? Well, I feel that calling. It's like someone has grabbed me by my jacket front and is pulling me towards the church. When I pray, I'm at peace and the hell of the war is behind me and all I see is the good I can do ahead of me. If that's not what God is, then I don't know what is. I don't expect you to exactly understand but perhaps you can get a flavour of what it is I'm experiencing?

I have some further news for you and this news is going to be a little harder to take. I've had a talk to May and Ken, and while Ken doesn't think now is the right time, May and I do! As you know, we are very much a socialist family and two to one will always be two to one.

There's no easy way of saying this but I'm not your real brother, I'm your cousin. So are Ken and May. We're all your cousins. Mum and Dad, God bless them, aren't your mum and dad. Sorry, this must be a massive shock to you so, to be clear, Marie Holmes, born Marie Scott, and David Holmes are your aunty and uncle. The person you call Mum is the sister of your real mum. I've written this a thousand times and it never reads right.

I wanted to tell you before you married Lizzie, but the others outvoted me. You're married now and when you get home, you'll be having family of your own, I guess, so you need to know. It doesn't change anything as far as we are all concerned. We love you as a brother and always will, well, to us, you are our brother. When you get home, I'll fill you in on the rest of it but for now I think I've explained as much as I can, the best I can, in a letter.

James, the other thing is, as well, we know who your real mum is as it's Mum's sister, Aunty Elsie, but we don't know who your dad is. I guess you need to speak to Aunty Elsie, your real mum, and find out when you come home. As you know, we've never had much to do with her since my mum died, and I guess you know why now. She's your real mum, James, and she's remarried, and you have three other half-brothers and sisters living on the outskirts of St Helens.

I'm sorry you had to find out this way but the teachings of the god whom I'm about to entrust the rest of my life with are pretty big on honesty. I couldn't be true to you or myself anymore without telling you.

We all love you very much.
Always your brother,

Frank

St Helens, Merseyside

1975

"So, sorry, Dad, just so I understand, who exactly adopted you?"

"It was my Aunty Marie. My true mum's sister."

"And what happened to her?"

"Well, it was tough in those days. My mum and dad, and I have always called them that and always will, both died when I was thirteen and fourteen years old. Dad went first of consumption and then Mum had some sort of wasting disease. They think it was cancer, but nobody actually said that then."

James Holmes was finishing off the seemingly never-ending stream of questions that his recently turned fourteen-year-old son was throwing at him like hand grenades.

"And what were their names?"

"Mum was Marie Holmes and dad was David Holmes."

"And you named our David after him?"

"Sort of. It was a name that your mum had lined up anyway. You were named after Graham Hill the racing driver. You can blame him for being called Graham."

"Never mind me. I'm just trying to work out who is who. It's like an episode of *Coronation Street*. So, when the people you called Mum and Dad died, what happened to you? Is that what these papers are all about?"

James was saddened that his son wasn't exactly grasping the situation.

"No, Graham, those papers are from when I was a baby and my mum's sister, Marie, took me as her own. Your Aunty May then brought up me and Ken with Frank's help when our parents died. We had the house in Harris Avenue."

"But Aunty May isn't my real aunty now, is she?" Graham was starting to get annoyed as the different pieces began to make some sense to him. His dad recognised the flare in his son's eyes as it was the same spark of anger that he had been trying to hold in check all of his life.

"You must never say that, Graham. Aunty May will always be your aunty, and Ken will be your uncle. If Frank were still alive, he would be your uncle also. They always treated you, Anne and David as their nephews and niece, and that will never change."

"But it has to change because it's not true, is it?" The spark had lit the flame now and it would be a while before the fire became under control.

Graham couldn't understand why he was feeling anger. For sure, he thought he was upset but was he faking it? Did he feel he had to be upset because that's what would be expected of him? This further caused him anger and pain because he believed he just couldn't be true to himself. But internally he wasn't sure what he was feeling.

James kindly gave his son the opportunity to digest the

unpalatable meal that had been presented to him.

"So, where's your real mum now, my real grandma?" Graham's father coldly raised his head and, making sure he had strong eye contact with his bewildered son, said, "I don't know, and I don't care!" The answer shocked Graham.

"But is she still alive?" pleaded Graham. And this was the first time in the conversation that James lied to his son.

"I have heard that she passed away, but I've also heard she's still living local to St Helens, but I've never followed either story up." James knew exactly where his birth mother was, and also knew she was very much alive. He had been caught off guard by the unveiling of the adoption documents and thought that he was 'doing right' by everyone by dealing with matters in this way. In his eyes, she was dead. To James Holmes, his own mother died the day that she handed him over to her sister to be raised as her sister's own son. In James's eyes, he had been abandoned and didn't want to even see her face ever again.

More questions were brewing inside the fourteen-year-old's brain.

"But what happened during your childhood? Did you not have a clue?"

"I was James Holmes. Son of David and Marie Holmes. Brother of Frank, May and Ken Holmes. My mum was one of at least seven, as many babies died young or were stillborn in those days, and I had aunties and uncles everywhere. I just didn't know my real mum was just another one of them. I treated her like I would any of my aunties, but to be honest we saw very little of her as I was growing up, and it took that letter from Frank for me to realise why! She didn't even want to see me."

Graham paused. They were sat in the dining room of their semi-detached house in Redpool, a district of relatively new builds put up in the early '60s on the outskirts of St Helens that had been James and Lizzie's second house after his National Service had finished. They were on either side of a highly polished wood table surrounded by six uncomfortable straight-backed chairs. The table reflected the woodchip-covered walls, painted a pale green. A cheap drinks cabinet sat off to one side of them with each of the large shelves holding a section of the very popular and expensive Hi-Fi system. An amp, a turntable, a radio, a cassette player and two speakers, but for today's conversation, no music played.

They looked at each other from either side of the table as though in an interview. Graham wondered if he was being interviewed or was, in fact, the interviewer.

"Your real mum has been alive all these years and living close by and you never wanted to see her?" Graham still had trouble getting his head around the situation.

"No, I didn't and never will, if she's still alive. She didn't want me. She just handed me over. What mother would do that to her only son? Just give him up like she did. I don't understand her and never will. Not only did she give me up, she never told me. But for me marrying your mum and Frank joining the priesthood, I might have never known. I didn't want to see her when I read the letter, I don't want to see her today and I don't want to see her tomorrow. It's gone too long now. It can't be mended, and I'm simply not bothered."

Once again, silence invaded the privacy of the life laid bare on the polished table.

"Can I find out if she's alive and wants to see me?" The words escaped Graham's mouth like leaves falling from a tree on an autumn morning. A whispered enchantment that if spoken aloud may come true.

"NO. It's over. I promised myself that I or your mum or any of my kids would never have anything to do with the woman. Trust me, Graham, no good can come from it. You've found out and I trust you with it but, no, you can't dig it all up again." James wasn't shouting but his words were strong and powerful and he trembled with years of pent-up emotion, and his son was under no illusion that today was not the day to try and change his dad's mind.

"Okay, okay. I get it. What about Anne and David?"

"They don't need to know yet. They're not old enough. Please keep this to yourself. I don't want everyone in the town talking about it." Graham nodded.

"Promise me, Graham."

"I promise." It was the son's turn to lie back to his father on this occasion.

"So, who's your dad, Dad? My grandad?"

"I don't know, and I guess we'll never know because I'll never ask her. All I know is, whoever the swine was, he made me a bastard. It could be anybody. She worked away in service somewhere. Then she came home, had me and you know the rest. Not a lot to go on, I know, but you'll just have to live with it like I've had to. As far as you're concerned, your paternal grandparents died when I was still a kid, and nothing has changed. You didn't have a grandad and grandma on your dad's side and still don't. Just get on with it, Graham, and don't let it bother you. You didn't know before today and it wasn't an issue. You needed boots to go and play some footy today and you'll need them again tomorrow. Me and your mum are still here, and Anne and David and Nana and Grandad Prescott, and your world hasn't changed. Don't let it become an issue. I haven't." And that was the second lie that James told his son that day.

St Helens

1975

An essay by Graham Holmes (aged 14)

I am alone, slowly walking through a never-ending cascade of glittering light. That was how I started this stupid English essay. Biggzy told me I had to write stories all the time if I wanted to be a writer. Not just when he tells me to. Is that one o or two? Doesn't matter as no one will read this anyway.

Under the stairs, that's where it was. The documents that leave me discombobulated as Ken Dodd would say. Aunty May loves Ken Dodd, but she's not my aunty now, she's not Dad's sister anymore, or Ken and Frank (who died ages ago in 1971 playing golf) his brothers.

Anyway, I was looking under the stairs for a pair of boots and I found a box from an old pair of shoes. I love rooting under the stairs as it's like a different world. No light, little corners full of stuff that's been there years.

I always dreamt I would find some treasure that would make us all rich. Well, I found something all right, but no one's getting rich.

Unless I have a grandad and grandma out there who have a big house somewhere posh like London. Who knows? Dad certainly doesn't know and doesn't want anyone else to know.

But the real question is, WHO THE HELL AM I? Dad's had years to cope with this but I've only had a day. The box was full of documents, insurance policies, birth certificates, really cool stuff.

I wish I had paid more attention to it because it's gone now and I didn't take it all in. There was another name on it but I honestly can't remember it. There was Dad's birth certificate with the dad bit left blank and then there was the adoption certificate, if that's such a thing, and that had a different name on it. BUT WHAT WAS IT?

I'm writing this really fast now and my writing is getting worse and worse. I wish I could do my homework this fast. Anyway, only me and Dad knows. I don't know if he told Mum I found them but he told me not to talk to anyone about it, not even Mum, and especially not Anne and David.

So I've got no one to talk to about it even if I wanted to. And I think I do. I feel sad but excited at the same time. I wanted to tell Charlie, he's my best mate and older than me, but Dad said I really couldn't tell anyone outside of the family. I actually think it's a cool story but when Dad said bastard to me I knew he was serious.

So what do I do? I actually think it's fantastic that I might have another real grandma and grandad out there to go with Nana and Grandad Prescott. But Dad won't even tell me her name and doesn't know his dad's name.

I am a bit confused, though, as Dad is still really angry all these years later because everyone kept a secret about him and he only found out in a letter, but he's now doing exactly the same thing and keeping a secret from everyone else. If I hadn't found the documents, he wouldn't have told me yet. And Anne and David don't know, but keeping the secret is what has upset Dad so much over the years.

If he could talk to his mum properly and not fall out with her, perhaps he could understand exactly what happened and why. And perhaps he could find out who his dad is.

I would love it if he did.

OK, Biggzy, I have done some writing but you can never see it. I'll go back to never-ending cascade of glittering light. Meanwhile, we are all off to the swimming baths tomorrow but Mush can't come because he's got verrucas.

Bye for now.
Locky!

Burnley, Lancashire

1937

Christmas had come and gone and Elsie had heard not a word nor read a letter from her estranged lover. After they had made love under the stairs and returned to the party, the rest of the evening panned out as might have been expected. Most people drank too much, especially Cook, who slept on a kitchen chair with her head on the table, waking in the darkness with a spot of pudding stuck to her cheek. Everyone else made it to bed and James left for his bed and breakfast with the promise that he would be back for Christmas, a promise that to this day remained broken.

Elsie wasn't overly worried as they arrived at the end of January. James had had to go this long before without being able to contact her. What was worrying Elsie more was the fact that she had missed her last period or, as she called them, her monthlies. She had no one to share her plight with. (She did consider telling Dot but that thought lasted as long as the life of a mayfly in summer.) Her mum was back home, although she didn't believe she could share such news with her anyway.

Life had seemed so good in December, but the world was darkening around her in the year of 1937. Why had she not heard from James? What was she to do if she was pregnant? She decided that rather than just sit and worry, she should do something; always better to take control rather than wait and hope, she thought. The others around her at work, mostly the ladies, Dot, Cook and Mrs Dawson, had seen a gradual change in Elsie as the end of January arrived with a roar of snow. December had been wonderful, full of love and as much pleasure as those in service to others were allowed to take.

Christmas came but James didn't. New Year came but still no sign of James Knowles. Elsie tried not to be concerned, or at least tried not to show it, but to those who knew her, she did. She got a Christmas card from her mum and dad and those of her family who still lived at home, but that was as far as the Christmas spirit stretched in her old household. By the time the snow started on Thursday, 28th January, the worry was etched on her face, now as much about the potential pregnancy as the missing James.

She buttoned her flimsy winter coat up to the top and wrapped a thick woollen scarf around her neck. Cook let her borrow a knitted bob hat to keep out any further cold and Elsie set off for Burnley Road and the Morris garage and showroom. Trudging through the slushy snow proved to be too much for her cheap and inadequate footwear and before she reached the end of the drive, her feet were soaking wet and throbbing with the cold. It would be worth it, she thought, if she had some news of James. She could remember the name of the old mechanic who sometimes helped out in the showroom, 'Fred'. He would help her, she hoped.

She arrived at the grand entrance furnished with the three show cars, polished so hard that the pale winter sunlight reflected around the showroom like light hitting a glitterball. Elsie took a deep breath of frosty air and pushed open the door. She half expected a little tinkle of a bell in imitation of the greengrocer's, but the Morris showroom wouldn't endorse such crudities. When that door opened, the sales staff had to be ready and pounced on suspected customers like policemen grabbing a shoplifter. Elsie was startled by the greying, besuited and Brylcreemed middle-aged man who promptly appeared at her elbow and said, "I think you've wandered into the wrong shop, miss. The butcher's is two doors down." Elsie had proven to herself many times in her life that she could face up to such sexist bullying and did so once again.

"No, sir, I have the right premises and I'm here to see Mr Knowles."

"Well, I'm sorry but Mr Knowles doesn't work here anymore."

Elsie was shocked and lost her head a little.

"But he must do, he would have told me if he had left." The salesman raised his eyebrows in an expression of 'here we go again'.

"I can assure you, miss, that Mr Knowles no longer works for Morris Cars. Either in Burnley or London. And for your information, he didn't leave his job. He was sacked." Elsie felt like she was spinning on the spot and felt a little sick. All pretence of cool had dissipated like her breath in the freezing wind.

"Sacked. Why?"

"He didn't show up for work second week of December last year. No one's seen hide nor hair of him since. He's scarpered. I don't wish to be rude, miss, but he's no great loss. I always thought he was all mouth and no trousers, if you know what I mean? Johnny-come-lately up from London. He won't be missed much in these parts."

Elsie thought the salesman was talking about someone else. This didn't sound like the James she knew and loved. She thought she was going to faint. She vaguely heard the salesman saying, "Are you all right, miss? You've gone a little pale." She nodded and, clutching her frail coat to her chest like a protective shield, she mumbled her thanks and stumbled back out into the freezing January air. She bumbled along the High Street totally forgetting the other errands she had to run while she was in town. Back down the drive, she was soon in the relative safety of the kitchen, trembling on a chair in front of Cook and Mr Dawson.

Mr Dawson showed no sympathy whatsoever to the shocked young woman visibly shaking in front of him.

"Elsie, Elsie, where are the groceries you went for? We have a dinner to prepare for this evening." For once, Dawson's authority was snatched away from him by Cook.

"Can you not see, Mr Dawson, that she is having problems of a delicate nature?" That was all it took for Dawson to leave to find Dot and send her back into town for the missing articles. Cook was no fool and gave Elsie a small tot of brandy. Firstly, to help what looked like a state of shock and, secondly, to simply warm her up. Elsie wasn't in tears, they would come later; she was just trembling uncontrollably. Cook very gently asked her if there was anything she wanted to tell her.

Elsie nodded and sipped the brandy, feeling the warmth spread down her burning throat and nestle comfortably in the pit of her stomach.

"I think I'm going to need some help, Cook. James has gone."

"What do you mean, he's gone? He's back in London, is all. We all know that."

"No, he's gone from London, and no one knows where." Elsie took the last of the brandy.

"Girl, I am concerned for you as I can see you're distressed, but please try to explain yourself a little better." Cook would help but her fuse was short, and she was easily frustrated.

"According to that bloke he works with at the Morris garage, James didn't show up for work in December and hasn't been seen since. By anyone."

"And that's what's caused all this fuss?" Cook saw a missing man as no reason for this sort of behaviour. "How do we know who's seen James and who hasn't? The bloke you refer to, the Morris salesman, doesn't get further than Burnley's town limits, so how does he know?"

"We know he's not been to work."

"So what? Fellas are leaving jobs all the time and looking for new ones. He might have got a better job."

"Well, why hasn't he told ME?" questioned the now slightly raised voice of Elsie.

Cook took a deep breath and said the obvious to her but

not obvious to Elsie. "Perhaps, young lady, he hasn't told you because he doesn't want you to know."

"But that's not possible, Cook. He told me he loved me. You saw him propose to me." Cook shook her head disconcertedly.

"It happens, love. Men, and women for that matter, say all sorts of things in passion that they later regret. Anyway, you're worrying yourself unduly. I'm sure he'll be speeding down that drive in a new car any day soon."

Elsie looked up at the gruff face but kindly eyes of Cook and with tears now starting to brim and spill like an overfull water font said, "God, I hope so, Cook, because I think I'm carrying his baby!"

Croydon, London

9th December 1936

Ludwig Hautzmayer was born on 25 April 1893 in Furstenfeld, Austria, but by his twenty-first birthday in 1914 was a reserve infantry officer in the Great War. Prior to joining the infantry, he had studied Mechanical Engineering at the Technical University in Graz. Always a keen sportsman, he enjoyed motorcycle racing, mountaineering and swimming but on the 8th of September 1914 suffered a severe leg wound that effectively ended his sporting days. After a lengthy recovery period taking him to March 1915, he transferred to the Austro-Hungarian Aviation Troops as an aerial observer. After forty combat missions on the Eastern Front, he underwent fighter pilot training. He became a World War I flying ace and was credited with seven aerial victories during his time as a pilot.

He became one of the best fighter pilots in the squadron after being posted to the Isonzo Front and was appointed commander of his own fighter squadron, Flik 61J. He was one of the few reserve officers so entrusted as a leader. At the end of the war, he received multiple decorations, all the way up to the Order of Leopold. Once the war was over, he left the forces and joined a commercial airline as a pilot for Malert.

On the 9th of December 1936, Hautzmayer was the pilot of a KLM airliner taking off from Croydon Air Port on a scheduled flight to Amsterdam, Holland. The Douglas DC-2 was carrying thirteen passengers including Arvid Lindman, a former prime minister of Sweden, and Juan de la Cierva, the Spanish inventor of the autogyro. The Douglas airliner was also supported by four crew, one of which was the pilot. By the end of the day, only two of the seventeen people on board would be alive.

The plane piloted by Hautzmayer was one of several departures that day and earlier a Swissair DC-2 had already successfully taken off. The issue with Croydon Air Port on the 9th of December 1936 was that it was shrouded in a thick fog, and visibility in places fluctuated between twenty-five and fifty yards. The fog also affected the acoustics and the planes loomed out of the fog, their engines echoing around the airport like prehistoric animals lowing in the gloom. In 1936, all aircraft operated under IFR, or Instrument Flight Rules, most important when airport weather conditions were as bad as they were that fateful day.

Effectively, the question that was being asked of the pilot and his crew was, 'Is the flight under Instrument Flight Rules (IFR) compulsory at Croydon?'

The answer to the query was yes, and all operations had to be performed under IFR conditions. In practical terms, what this meant was that crews of all departing aircraft were following a white line laid out east to west on the grass surfaces of the runways marked for take-offs. This was normal procedure and was used extensively across the United Kingdom, and Croydon had been following this practice since 1931. In fact, the Swissair Douglas had departed twenty-five minutes earlier using the exact same methodology. There was absolutely no cause for concern, and in Ludwig Hautzmayer, the plane had one of the most experienced and decorated pilots flying at that time.

Hautzmayer manoeuvred the plane into position on the slick wet grass of the runway. The plane felt a little light in his hands but normal for the weather conditions. The DC-2 started its take-off chundering along the white line freshly painted for the flight. The plane was due to head out west over Sutton, but it never got that far. After two hundred yards, the plane veered off to its left, heading south instead of east. It became airborne but south was towards rising ground instead of its normal westerly direction. The pilot was clearly wrestling with the controls as the plane couldn't hold any height and was bobbing up and down like a fisherman's float on the water. Hautzmeyer managed to get the plane high enough to skirt over the fence marking the southern boundary of the airport.

The first obstacle the plane encountered was a house on Hillcrest Road, Purley. A wing of the plane dislodged the whole chimney and the bricks fell onto the walkway below, hurting several people, one seriously. Hitting the chimney damaged the flaps and now Hautzmayer had no control at all. The plane spun 45 degrees and straight into a house on the opposite side of Hillcrest Road. Luckily, both houses were empty at the time of the crash as the second house bore the brunt of the impact. The plane burst into flames, destroying the house and the adjoining one also. Within moments, the street was alive with emergency services but alas for fifteen of the people on board the DC-2, they had taken their last flight. Only two people survived: the flight attendant and the radio operator. One passenger made it to Purley Hospital but sadly lost his fight against his sustained injuries later that day.

When this crash happened, it was the worst air crash in the United Kingdom for fatalities on record and was the second plane to crash in fog while leaving Croydon Air Port by the 'white line' method. The first had been an Air France aircraft on the 31st of May 1934 that had hit an aircraft navigation beacon at the end of the runway, killing the two crew members instantly. The investigation into the greatest loss of life ever experienced due to a plane crash in the United Kingdom was terminated later that month on the 16th of December. The investigation never reached a verdict.

The debris falling into the street hit several pedestrians, but the majority had minor injuries that could be treated on the spot or in the accident and emergency section of Purley Hospital on Pampisford Road, a five-minute drive from where the houses were hit by the plane. One man was hit particularly hard and knocked unconscious and it was a close call as to whether he would survive. He was non-responsive for several days and was kept stable until he could be taken off life support. The majority of the brickwork from the chimney had landed directly on him and so there was some thought as to whether he would ever recover completely at all. It was Tuesday, 27th April 1937, 138 days later, when James Knowles regained consciousness and the first word he said was "Elsie."

The unknown name worried his already devastated wife and child, who were sat by his side, but at least her husband and her son's father was speaking again.

Toronto, Canada

2019

Anne didn't like international travel. She didn't like driving a long distance along the motorways of England, either. In fact, she wasn't a fan of walking to the corner shop for a paper. She liked her walks around Christleton Pond with Colin when they had time together and he managed to stay at home for longer than three days. Flying to Toronto in Canada, all on her own, was a journey too far. The person waiting for her at the other end, she hoped, was Melanie Belanger. What an exotic name that sounded to her, especially since she'd changed from Holmes to Smith. It was Melanie's married name as she had been born Knowles, a name that didn't have any special meaning to Anne in her search for her paternal grandfather.

Anne had finally come to terms with the reason for undertaking this flight of fantasy, as she was calling her trip to Canada. It wasn't because she was bored or had time on her hands or needed a hobby, as her mother suggested. It was because since Dad had died, she simply wanted to know where she originally came from. He never wanted to know but she did, and the older she was getting, the greater the priority. *Who am I?* This was the thought that now kept her awake at nights.

She had driven from home to the airport first thing in the morning, taking the A556 through Northwich and Knutsford in order to avoid as much of the motorways as possible. It took her slightly longer, but she was prepared to accept that inconvenience for the living hell that was the M56. Her lunchtime Lufthansa flight direct to Toronto had taken off promptly and she was scheduled to land in an hour at approximately three in the afternoon Toronto time. As close to time travel as currently existed in 2019.

Melanie Belanger, the lady with a close DNA match to her. She had looked Belanger up on her beloved Google and it meant, 'Beautiful or divine anger'. Anne was not exactly clear what that meant in English even after the translation from its French origin. So, drilling further down, divine anger is, 'the anger of a king or deity that has no feeling in it but should be the proper response to a public wrong'. Anger that has no feeling or hatred in it. The plane was sashaying down onto the runway now and Anne shut her eyes. She was thinking, *My anger is divine. I have no hatred or real feeling against anyone. I just want to know who I am. I can't hate someone in the past for what they thought was right at the time. I just want to know who that person was making the decisions and why they made them.* The plane bumped off the runway, creating a collective intake of breath followed by nervous giggles and laughter from the passengers, including

Anne. Her line of thought was interrupted as she looked out of the window across the two people on her inside. She was here, and that in itself was a big step.

"Call me Mel," said Melanie Belanger. Anne nodded, overawed by the parcel of brimming confidence in a pork pie hat stood in front of her. Mel was smaller than Anne but not by much and for once Anne didn't feel she was towering over the person she was with. Mel had the same long blonde hair as Anne, but she wore it loose and with various different colours blended in. Anne's was tied back in a ponytail for convenience. Mel had the same bright eyes as Anne and a younger, less worn-out face that must have been a good twenty years younger. Her makeup was finished off with a slash of bright red lipstick that Anne would have described as garish. (Later, Anne would be disappointed to find out that Mel was only fourteen years her junior and promised herself better skincare when she got home. Colin could whistle at the expense.)

Anybody seeing the two come together in an awkward embrace, made awkward by Anne, not Mel, would immediately see the family resemblance. Anne saw it and was momentarily overwhelmed, tears welling in the corners of her eyes that she tried to quell but couldn't. Both Mel and Anne thought they looked like each other but Mel was aware that the power of suggestion was strong, and they were both very keen to make that connection. Hugs over and out of the way, Mel led them through the airport. She took them to a big Volkswagen four-wheel drive, one that Anne wouldn't have liked to operate, and sped away from the airport while at the same time pointing things out to Anne and supplying her with a stream of questions that she didn't really wait for any answers to. This was going to be a long four days.

What Anne wasn't aware of at this point was that Mel was overcompensating for her own lack of confidence. One failed marriage and a string of failed relationships behind her, with both men and women, Mel's stream of consciousness was her own defence mechanism to combat meeting new people for the first time. Add to the mix that Anne may well be a long-lost relative and she defaulted to a motor mouth with delusions of self-confidence.

Eventually, Anne managed to ask a few questions of her own.

"So, what do you do for a living?"

"I'm one of the curators at the Gardiner Museum. Have you heard of it? No, well, it's one of the biggest pottery, china and ceramics museums in the world. It's on Queens. It was opened in 1984 by George Gardiner himself. He was a famous stockbroker who used to chair the Toronto stock exchange and made a lot of money. He used to collect ceramics as a hobby and then decided to open the museum. It's now one of the biggest in the world. But I've said that. Anyway, I help to pull together exhibitions there." This whole brain dump was said in the one breath.

Anne tried to make conversation, although for her it was much later in the day and she wasn't one for napping, not even on a flight after a couple of gin and tonics. Generous gin and tonics as well. As her mum often said when offered a drink, "Gin and tonic, please, and I like to taste the gin."

Anne asked, "Where do you live in Toronto?" As soon as she asked the question, she realised she knew nothing about the areas or districts of Toronto and this conversation was going to die on the vine before it had chance to bloom. Luckily for Anne, Mel didn't need much encouragement.

"Okay then. I'll assume you don't know too much about Toronto so please stop me when you've had enough. As I said, I work at the Gardiner Museum, which is situated in the district called Downtown. Every city in Canada and America has a downtown and historically it sounds like it's a poor or unsavoury part of a city but that isn't always the case. These days, people just say downtown as the southern part of the city. Anyway, I work in Downtown, one of ten districts that make up Toronto, and I know what you're going to ask me now." Mel looked expectantly at Anne. Anne obliged; it was her personal superpower after all.

"What are the other nine?" Anne completed the tableau by raising her eyebrow like a dastardly Dickensian villain.

"Well, I'm glad you asked, Anne. I had to learn these by rote when in school and I've never forgotten. They are North York, York-Crosstown and East York. Then East End, Midtown and West End. Then the big ones, Etobicoke, and where I live, Scarborough. Plus, Downtown makes ten!" Mel smiled as though she had predicted the winning lottery numbers.

"That's only nine," said Anne (who sadly had been counting), helpfully holding nine fingers in the air just in case Canada used a different decimal system to the United Kingdom.

Mel frowned.

"I'm sure that's ten, I've been doing that parlour trick all my life." Anne couldn't let this go. All her life she had stood on the touchline cheering on the rest of the world and now she had thrust herself into the game, she had to be honest to herself.

"Do it again then and we'll count them off together," suggested Anne, wondering why she was trying to make an enemy of this person she had just met. The person who could be the key to unlocking the missing parts of her jigsaw of a family tree.

Mel did her party piece once more and Anne raised a digit for every one named. This time, Mel got it right, but she wasn't smiling second time around.

"North York, York-Crosstown, East York, East End, West End, Uptown, Midtown, Downtown, and the big ones, Etobicoke and Scarborough, where we are going now because that's where my house is! That's ten." Anne looked down at her fingers and indeed, as if by magic, she had ten fingers (and thumbs) held up.

"Sorry," she said, falling back into the habit of her lifetime, apologising for being correct.

"That's okay, Anne, it's all new to you and you must be tired after such a long journey. Let me tell you a little bit about Scarborough.

"Scarborough has always been the home for new people entering the city of Toronto, especially since the end of the Second World War. It's a real lively and diverse place to live, with people settling down here from all over the world. As my mom used to call it, not unkindly, 'Immigrant central'. Another really good thing about Scarborough is the cost of living. The difference in prices between buying a house where I live versus living downtown is almost double. Plus, you get the best weather.

"Scarborough's climate is moderate compared to the rest of Canada, due to its southerly location and its closeness to Lake Ontario. We get warm, sticky summers but generally cold winters. I like that you still get the proper seasons in Scarborough. On average, it's slightly colder than Downtown because of our proximity to the lake; that's what people say. And as I said, we do get cold, foggy days in winter."

Anne was impressed with her (hopefully) distant relative's knowledge of her home city.

"How do you know all this stuff?"

"Oh, I'm only just getting started. I did Canadian History for my master's after getting my original degree in just History. I've made it my duty to learn about where I'm from and how it came to be. That's how I happen to be on the same website that you're on. I just want to know more. For example, did you know that Scarborough is named after the same place in England, in Yorkshire?"

"I did wonder," answered Anne. "After all, it is quite a unique name."

"Oh yes, listen to this, it goes all the way back to the eighteenth century. The area was named by Elizabeth Simcoe, the wife of the first lieutenant governor of Upper Canada. The bluffs along Scarborough's Lake Ontario shores reminded her of the limestone cliffs in Scarborough, England, where she had come from. Before that, it was named Glasgow, after the Scottish city, but Scarborough stuck and it's still Scarborough today. Isn't it fascinating how names come about?"

Anne noticed that Mel had almost started to glow with pride because of her heritage and also the pride of knowing the details so well that she could share them with visitors to her birthplace. She also thought that if she ever had to take Mel around England, she would need a crash course in local History. Perhaps Graham's daughter Susan could help her as she'd studied History at Exeter University.

Mel paused for breath and a comfortable silence settled over the two of them. Anne could feel the onset of waves of tiredness envelop her as her travels started to take their toll. The car journey was not a long one, though, as Mel lived in a place called Agincourt, which once clear of Toronto Pearson International Airport was only a thirty-minute drive. It was now approaching 5pm local time.

The house was on Marilyn Avenue, a suburban road of large, mostly white wooden homes, which to Anne looked like oversized barns. A wide concrete drive led up to a double garage built into the house with an expansive picture window set above it.

"That's your room above the garage, Anne. I don't have many guests but that's what I call my guest room. I hope you're going to like it. This is what I can afford with my half of the divorce monies. It's a few years old and needs some work, but it's large and lets me work on my ceramics when I'm not talking about them at the museum. This is me and it's lovely to have you here. Between us, we may be able to shine a light on the past and hopefully it doesn't cast too deep a shadow on our present. Come on, let's get you settled."

Anne was almost reduced to tears. This wasn't going to be any hardship. She may talk a lot and fiercely guard her own space in the world, but kindness oozed from Mel like cream from a cake. For the first time since buying the ticket for the flight, Anne felt good about her decision to go to Canada.

The next morning was a Saturday and although Mel would normally have gone to the museum, she had planned her weekend around the visit from her new English acquaintance, or should that be relative? Mel would have been lying if she said she wasn't somewhat disappointed with the seemingly downbeat and quiet, spindly lady from northern England. She decided to give her the benefit of the doubt as it was a long trip, and she was only here for a couple of days. Plus, the true reason for the meet was to try and ascertain if they were indeed related in some way or form. Facially, there was a definite likeness, but were they seeing what they wanted to see as the resemblance stopped jarringly once blonde, pretty and high cheekbones were taken out of the equation?

The day was bright, clear, a little chilly, but with the promise of warmth as the day wore on. The night before, Mel had prepared a tuna salad with fruit and cream for dessert, but Anne hadn't eaten much and pushed it around her plate. If Mel had been the mother of the child, Anne would have been sent to bed with no fruit and cream. As it was, the dessert was wolfed down by Anne as if someone was going to steal it off her plate. Mel did most of the talking, giving a potted history of her own life.

She had travelled before marrying, spending time in London, Inner Mongolia in China teaching English and had even spent a summer in Norway, just because she could. She married an American man, Brett Belanger, who she had met on her travels in Disneyland, Florida. Brett's family were originally French Canadian, so they hit it off straight away. She was working Space Mountain at the time, while he played Woody from *Toy Story* all day long. It was meant to be, for at least four years anyway, before they shook hands and went their separate ways. No children came from the experience, as Mel saw it, but living with a man-child for four years had put her off them for life, and she saw no reason to wish another child on the crumbling society of the northern hemisphere.

She devoted herself to her job at the museum and loved ceramics with a passion, such that if she had introduced the same energy to her marriage, it might have been more successful. These thoughts she openly suggested herself to Anne, opening up in a way that Anne would never be able to do even if she had known her new 'friend' for five years, and not five hours. They deliberately chose not to discuss their families at this point of the Friday night, saving the 'big' conversation for the next day. Anne had retired to bed as late as she could manage, trying her utmost to get on Canadian time so she could try and enjoy the long weekend as much as possible.

The bright Saturday morning thrilled them both as Mel drove her station wagon to Rouge National Urban Park. A fifteen-minute trip down the 401, eventually following the Rouge River, after which the park was named. Mel, as had already become the custom, filled Anne in on the local history and information.

"First of all, Anne, there is a 'lot' of history at Rouge Park, and I could bore you for hours with it, but you'll be happy to hear that I won't. I'll just give you a very potted history." When Anne heard the emphasis on the word 'lot', her shoulders visibly sagged, but Mel didn't, or perhaps chose not to, react.

"The first thing to know is that settlers first arrived here at the Rouge River Park region in 1799. Since then, the land has been used for many contrasting functions before becoming what it is today, a national park. If we were to spend a week wandering around here, you would see some of the settlements that have existed over the last two centuries, but you still wouldn't see them all. So, all you need to know is that originally the land was used to build and support communities of immigrants from Europe, but the indigenous races were here for centuries before then. There, that wasn't so bad, was it?" Anne felt guilty but smiled supportively.

"Today, we are just going to enjoy the views and the environment. We're going to walk for an hour or so, stop and have a picnic and then we can have our 'serious' talk. I felt it was good to get to know each other better before embarking on genealogies! All you will need are those hiking shoes and your sense of adventure." Anne looked like she had been asked to cut her own throat and jump in the lake. Mel was not perturbed.

"You can come here any time of the year and there are natural, cultural and agricultural areas to explore. We've not got a guide as you've got me, but I do have a canoe stored here and we can drift through the marshes later if you like. It's not full fall yet but the leaves are starting to turn, and you will get some great photos of the sun glowing in the golden leaves. Anne, this is really a 'people's park', just waiting for you to enjoy it. You can take from it whatever you want."

Anne pulled on her hiking boots and a rucksack with water and some provisions. Mel had prepared everything for her, and the two set off into the park. What awaited them was simply an amazing exposure to the type of nature that Anne had no opportunity to ordinarily experience. The park was a rich assembly of natural landscapes, one of the region's largest marshes, a beach at Lake Ontario, many wonderful hiking opportunities and human history dating back over 10,000 years, including some of Canada's oldest known indigenous sites.

After walking for just over an hour, they arrived at a bluff overlooking the lake and it became too much for Anne and she slumped down onto a viewing bench.

"Sorry, Mel, getting a little tired now with the jet lag and the walk. I'm coming up to fifty-six years old in a couple of months."

"That's no problem. Fifty-six years young, not old, Anne. You've probably chosen one of the best views of the lake to have a rest anyway. You may not have noticed but we have been on something of a circular route and we're about ten minutes away from the car and our picnic lunch. So, take your time and then we'll go and get something to eat."

They sat in silence, peaceful, the only sounds the cries of the varied birdlife, some behind them in the forest and others spiralling above the lake on upward helixes before twisting and diving to the lake's surface. If they left empty-clawed, then the process would start again. Anne thought the upwards spiral was Monday to Friday then the quick dive and splash the weekend, before starting again with nothing to show for it on the following Monday. So much for the 'Circle of Life' that cartoon lions sang about! She didn't see the sadness in the fact that she just couldn't sit and enjoy such incredible natural beauty without more than a hint of cynicism.

Thirty minutes later, they were sat in the wooded picnic area surrounded by tall sugar maples, the tree on the national flag of Canada, plus ironwood, white cedar and red oak. The cold had been burnt away and the turning trees glistened in the noonday sun. Not too hot, a little breeze and the majority of the walk behind them, their appetite had built nicely; it was the perfect setting and time for a leisurely lunch. The tables around them were mostly taken up by young families but not to the extent that it was so busy that they didn't have a choice. They sat with the food cooler and their laptop cases underneath the canopy of green, turning to brown leaves, of a magnificent red oak tree.

When Anne prepared a picnic at home for her and Colin or the girls and their partners, should they be there, it was pretty basic fare, but they knew what they liked. So, it would be cheese and ham sandwiches or as they had been brought up to say, 'butties'. Or beef with some Branston pickle, or egg and cream cheese or cheese and pickle. These would be supplemented with pork pies, scotch eggs, sausage rolls and if they were doing 'posh', wraps of some description. A flask of builder's tea and a bottle of water and they were 'away'.

Mel announced the food from her cooler with all the pomp of Lumière singing *Be Our Guest* in *Beauty and the Beast*.

"To delight your tastebuds today, Anne, I have gone a little over the top. I wouldn't normally prepare such a grand menu as today's when I'm on my own or with my girlfriends, but I will not lie to you. I have made more of an effort for your visit. It isn't very often I entertain long-lost relatives from the UK, or at the very least, potential long-lost relatives." Mel picked up a heavily packed tortilla wrap and started to peer into it like an inquisitive baby with a new toy.

"We have turkey club wraps. I found the recipe for these on a particular Canadian picnic website. I'll be honest, I didn't even know such things existed but included in these tortillas are… smoked turkey breast, cheddar cheese, crispy bacon strips, lettuce, this is romaine (Anne didn't have a clue what romaine lettuce was), small sliced tomatoes and finally avocado. Oh, and the dressing is ranch. Everything has to be sliced as thinly as possible. At least that's what it said on the website." Anne made a face that suggested she was suitably impressed while thinking, *So far, so Waitrose.*

Mel was on a roll. (Or was that a wrap?)

"I thought after a walk we might get a little hot, so I have some freshly made tomato gazpacho."

Cold soup, thought Anne, now beginning to think how unreasonable she was sounding even to herself. Mel forged onwards.

"A choice of salads. We have kale salad, roasted vegetable salad and asparagus potato salad. A fresh brown bread loaf and butter. It's not really butter, it's a low cholesterol spread, but you know what I mean. For dessert, we have a selection of fruit, cherries, grapes, strawberries and watermelon. And, to wash it all down, cucumber and mint water."

Mel looked at Anne with all the expectation of a groom on his wedding night. Anne felt a number of things all at once, but the overwhelming feeling was one of guilt for being so unkind. This lady, whom she had never met until yesterday, had gone to so much effort just to provide her with something nice to eat and a day to remember. She also felt joy, trepidation, sadness, wonderment and gratitude but as had happened so many times before in her life, Anne treated her feelings as intruders to be shut out, should they ever break through the barrier of her fear. Fear of living.

One thing Anne did have was manners, and she knew what she was supposed to say even if she wasn't sure what it was she should be feeling.

"Mel, thank you so much. You really shouldn't have gone to so much trouble just for me, but I can tell you I'm so glad you did. If we eat all this wonderful food, they'll have to roll us back to the car and squash us into the seats." They took their time eating and enjoying the food and the talk turned to what Anne did for a living. Mel seemed genuinely jealous of the relationships that Anne had built with her classroom children, expressing sadness that at forty-one she may have missed out on the chance of her own.

Anne in her turn was jealous of the intellectual challenges of Mel's role at the museum, where she curated pieces for particular exhibitions. She made many lectures during the year, both at the museum and Toronto University, and seemed to have to attend numerous conferences and dinners full of dignitaries, as part of her occupation. The two women seemed to be looking for excuses to talk or think about anything but the main reason they had chosen to meet up. Their two totally disparate and unconnected existences had been unceremoniously thrown together and they were politely pushing against the interference. Their lives may not have been perfect, but at least they were their own and didn't need justifying to anyone else. They were ready-made sounding boards for each other, but disparaging ones. By some cruel trick of genetics, their lives were being held up against each other for a comparison that was unjustified, impolite, almost indecent. They couldn't say it, but they felt strip-bared and pinned on the sample board ready for inspection.

Anne took the lead, reaching for her laptop.

"I'll show you as far as I've managed to get with the family tree, and you can tell me where you've got with yours. It's a bit of a tatty piece of paper but I prefer writing it out rather than using the website. You end up having to print about twenty-seven pieces of paper for one little tree." Mel came around to Anne's side of the picnic table and shushed up next to her.

"Talk me through it then, please, Anne," said Mel.

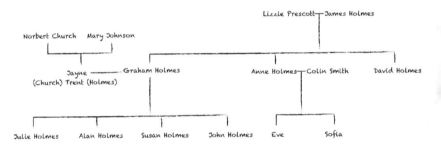

"Okay, top right. That's the grey bit of a hole punch. I never know what it's for but it's not part of my, sorry, 'our' family tree." Mel actually laughed out loud, much to Anne's surprise. Not a major breakthrough but a small step.

"So, James Holmes – my dad. Passed away two years ago or we wouldn't be having this conversation.

"Lizzie Prescott – Mum's maiden name.

"Then comes me, married to Colin. He won't be happy as I put him on here as an afterthought. When you try and write these things out, they get very messy. And my two girls, Eve and Sofia. Graham, my elder brother, and his four kids from his first marriage, now married to Jayne. She won't thank me for getting her name wrong. I always get Jayne and Julie mixed up; we call them senior moments in England. My younger brother, David, who has been married a few times, so I ran out of paper there.

"Then I have this page, which is all Mum's family."

Anne produced another sheet of paper ripped from a notepad with several levels going back through the generations of her maternal family tree. "But I don't know how to do Dad's side. This is the big family mystery. I think Graham knows more than he's letting on and Mum has told me a few things but…" Anne's words dried up. She had practised saying these words many times in her mind, but now she wanted to say them out loud they stuck in her throat like a tickle that you just can't clear.

"Here, have a look."

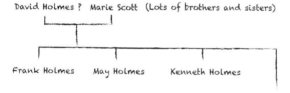

"There's Mum and Dad again at the bottom. Uncle Frank, Catholic priest, died in 1971; Aunty May died of a heart attack, 1983; Uncle Ken, heart attack as well, not sure of the date. Their dad, David Holmes, married Marie Scott. These two died when Dad was still little but, are they his parents?

We think not. According to Mum after a few wines, Dad was adopted. David and Marie Holmes are Dad's aunty and uncle. Marie had lots of brothers and sisters and one of them, we believe, is Dad's real mum.

"We're pretty sure on that one. The real question is, who was his dad, my grandad? And now we have you, Mel, and all your family, and your DNA and my DNA suggests we may be cousins or at least second cousins."

Mel had not spoken during all this time. Her brow was creased, and little worry lines appeared at the corners of her eyes. Anne then said, "Look at this photo of me on my wedding day." She was about to ask if Mel saw any resemblance, but Mel just covered her mouth with her hand. The girl in the photograph, resplendent in a glistening ivory wedding gown, could have been the sister of the girl born in Canada. There was no need for Anne to ask the question of Mel; the tears welling up in her eyes told Anne everything she needed to know. The two women hugged; they hugged like cousins who hadn't seen each other for a very long time.

Mel composed herself.

"I'll tell you what I know of my family story. Sometime in 1940, before Pearl Harbour and America's introduction into the war, my Grandad Knowles and two of his three brothers emigrated from England with their families to Toronto, to Scarborough. Two of them had families already, one of them didn't, but one brother was left in London.

"Eventually, each of their families grew up and met partners and they had kids as well. One of which was me. My mum was a native Canadian and she married my dad, who was aged two when he left England. The whole family chose to leave England, London, as the bombing started. My grandad and his two brothers both fought in the war but under the Canadian flag, ironically back in Europe.

"Our family mystery is the brother that never came. He was a messed-up kind of man, according to Grandad, after a nasty accident that left him mentally unwell. He chose to stay in London as he was 'waiting for someone'. His estranged wife died young, and his son went to America to start a new life. Allegedly, he just abandoned them. He even changed his name so no one could find him. My great-aunty Margaret, his wife, she died a long time ago, but I can't tell you when. How ironic is it that I can tell you anything about Canadian history or ceramics but don't know the detailed history of my own family?"

"Do you know his name, Mel?"

"Other than Knowles, no, sorry. They only seemed to have a small number of male names in those days. Everyone was either, John, Robert, James, William, Richard, Charles or George!" Anne was thinking there must be someone still alive who knew the names of Mel's great-uncles. Or perhaps the database of the genealogists that they were both using could have the secrets locked in its code?

"What about his wife, do you have any idea what happened to her side of the family? Didn't you say that she had a son?"

"She remarried an American boy and ended up in a big house in London, and that was either during the war or not long after it. Once again, she didn't keep in touch. Don't forget, Anne, in those days it was still mostly hand-written letters or the odd phone call if you were lucky enough to have a phone, that is. Plus, she had no reason to keep in touch. We weren't her real family. She had a couple of brothers-in-law but that was it. Once she had the option to provide her son with a father and make a new life for herself, she took it." Anne was getting frustrated.

"But, Mel, you're a historian. This is your bread and butter. Why have you not even tried to put together your family tree?"

"Why would I? My mum bought me this DNA test as a present and I dutifully did it and sent it away, but after I received the report back, I thought no more about it. It didn't tell me anything new or interesting. But answer the question yourself. You had your test for years before you used it. And you have a reason to use it. Your paternal grandfather is missing from your family tree and yet you didn't immediately react when Colin bought you the gift.

"Anne, we all have busy lives to live today without adding more stress and pressure to it. I finished my History degree nearly twenty years ago and now I'm into ceramics. For sure, history still interests me, but I've just not gotten around to building my tree."

Anne was exasperated because she knew Mel was right. "I'm sorry, Mel. I just feel we are so close to working this out."

Mel was not without compassion and said, "Let's pack up, go back to my house, where we have wi-fi, and spend the rest of your time here trying to find out as much as we can. I can at least devote the time while you're in Canada to finding as many answers as possible to questions you have." Anne merely nodded her assent, not letting her disappointment stay hidden.

By 9pm that evening, they had as much as they were going to glean from the Hereditary website.

Mel's grandad was called Joseph Knowles and his three brothers, Mel's great-uncles, were called William, known as Billy; Thomas; and the youngest, who stayed in England, was called James T Knowles. James remained hidden from his Canadian family by changing his name. When he died in the 1970s, the English solicitor dealing with the will was under strict legally binding orders to keep his new name and address from the family. The house where he lived was sold and after contributions to charities the money was sent to the eldest living male relative of the Knowles family based in Toronto to split equally amongst all living relatives.

To this day, no one had any idea what had happened to him or what life he had lived. His wife died and his child had vanished into the wilds of Texas with a new name and couldn't be traced through the records. They just weren't as well kept in some of the bigger states of America in the war years. James Knowles was as much a mystery to Mel's family as Anne's paternal grandfather was to hers. Somewhere, there was a very strong biological connection, but it couldn't be proven one way or the other.

According to the Hereditary website, there were strong odds (they stated that it was 30,000/1 against Anne and Mel not being related) that one of the four Knowles brothers could have been the grandfather of Anne Smith, born Holmes, and the father of James Holmes, Anne's recently deceased father. The evidence was strong but far from conclusive. Somewhere in Mel and Anne's joint histories was the clue to solve the eternal question, 'Who am I?'

On the Monday, the two women said their goodbyes as Mel dropped Anne off at the airport. They had jointly arrived at the conclusion that they would never know the truth. Why would James Knowles have abandoned his young family, his son, on the other side of the world, while he stayed in England? Anne held on to this one hope as she sat on the flight back home. She also had a couple of mementos that Mel had copied from her father's possessions that she could show to her mum when she got home.

If that proved to be fruitless then the search was over. Her dad's reluctance to share and to take the truth to his grave with him was what he must have wanted. Anne's father, James Holmes, didn't actually know much more than Anne had managed to unearth, so he hadn't taken too much truth with him. Anne felt so close and as she dozed off on the flight back to Manchester, thought, *I'll go around the family one more time and then that is it. I cannot let this search take over my life.* Five minutes later, she was snoring like a purring cat.

Old Road, Hampton

2007

Extracts From a Journal

September 14th

Friday. Hello, journal. I've been away. Making some life decisions – BIG ones. I decided to take Alan's advice. He's my older brother who wants to live in Japan, and he suggested to me that I should do the course he's been doing: 'Teaching English as a Foreign Language'. I do want to travel and get that out of my system. I'll always come back, too much of a homebird for staying away. Ok, got to go, Friday night. People to see, food to eat, drinks to drink.

September 22nd

Saturday. I've started my TEFL courses. Sorry, journal, 'Teaching English as a Foreign Language'. You say it 'teffle'. I can do stages two to four online at a fantastic price. Well, fantastic for me as Dad paid! One hundred and seventy hours. I'm aiming to do two hours a day plus eight over the weekend every week. I'll be qualified in ten weeks, give or take a week or two, and then I can start planning my trips. I know it's mad, but I've got a longing for Columbia!

September 23rd

Sunday. Had a long discussion with Dad that then turned into an argument. He said something along the lines of, "I'll burn your passport and all your clothes before I'll let you go to Columbia!" So, it looks like Columbia is off. One of my friends said it was really dangerous and she was told by a taxi driver to lie on the floor of his cab rather than let people see her blonde hair. Sounds like some suburbs of London I've been to. Columbia's off but China is still an option.

December 10th

Monday. QUALIFIED!!!!!!!

December 11th

Tuesday. I am never, ever, ever, ever doing Jager shots again. I don't think Dad was too chuffed the way I came in last night, but it is Christmas and I've qualified, and unbeknownst to him I've already applied to go to China. It's a place called Hohhot in Inner Mongolia. It's a city as big as Birmingham but that's on the small side, apparently, for a Chinese city. I will be travelling in early January, dates to be confirmed. One of the girls I did the course with, Emily, is coming with me. What a fantastic opportunity. But first I have to tell you something that happened when I got in late last night and, admittedly, I was drunk.

This is what happened. Don't forget I was smashed. Dad left me on the landing and, although he was annoyed, said good night and well done on my results and everything. To be fair to myself, I remember everything and if I'm really drunk that can become something of a blur. He had got up out of bed to come and pick me up so was straight back in, but I had makeup to take off and stuff to do that I always do when I come in late.

Into the bathroom, back into the bedroom, clothes off, folded neatly and dropped on the floor, back into the bathroom, teeth, bedroom, put some music on with my headphones in order to keep the peace. It was only 1.30am by this time. Then, even though I was wearing headphones, I heard it again. A ball bouncing against the wall. The wall that joined onto next door, but they had two teenage lads so it could have been one of them. Except it was in my headphones. And I was listening to one of my dad's favourites, *Bat out of Hell* by Meatloaf. Loud, loud, loud.

This time, alcohol fuelled, I wasn't as frightened and tried to look for an obvious answer, but none came to me. The sound, heard over the blaring of *Paradise by the Dashboard Light*, was of a rubber or tennis ball hitting the floor, then wall then pause. If you have seen Steve McQueen in *The Great Escape*, you'll know what I mean. And who hasn't seen it! It's on every Christmas.

I took the headphones off, but the sound didn't get louder, which made me think it was in my head and not for real. I sat on the edge of my bed and the pattern from last time repeated itself. The ball bounce got closer, and I swear it was just to my right as I sat on the bed. I was really frightened again but not so much that I had to jump up and run away to my brother's room. I spoke aloud the words that I've heard in so many films and television series: "Is there anybody there?" I don't know why I asked because an answer would have sent me running. The ball bounced and I stood up from the bed and moved past it to the bedroom door. The noise stopped and I went to the bathroom to get a drink of water, plus, I have to admit in the cold light of day, to move away from the sound.

The bathroom has a nightlight over the mirror above the sink so I didn't have to put the main light on, thinking it may wake others. My makeup-free pale face stared back at me out of the darkness behind. I bent and looked down to fill a glass with chilly water and mentally gave myself a good telling-off. One of the lads next door must be messing about in his bedroom late at night and all I was hearing were those noises, my brain translating them into something I wanted to hear. I didn't really want to hear a ball bouncing. So, translated them into something I expected to hear.

Face raised, looking into the mirror again, I didn't see it at first. Something pale behind my own pale face. Was it just my own face double reflected because of the nightlight? I squinted as the image moved forward. I looked behind me quickly but there was nothing there so turned back to the mirror.

The woman's face appeared out of nowhere, like an image out of the mist on a dark night.

I screamed. I shut my eyes and I screamed. Seconds later, the bathroom was full of people. Dad, Jayne and John. The usual round of *What's the matter?... Are you ok?... What's going on?* bounced off the tiled walls. No amount of explanation would divert Dad and John away from the alcohol (imagine if they'd known I'd been on the Jager bombs), but Jayne did not look as sceptical, God bless her.

I'm going to China after the New Year celebrations. Nothing could change my mind. I need a change of scenery where there's no bouncing balls or pale images in mirrors – other than my own.

I'm writing this now in my bedroom the next night and I'm looking at something Jayne gave me. She asked me, was this who I thought I had seen? I honestly don't know. It really could have been, but I don't know.

Anyway, China, here I come.

Burnley/Blackburn, Lancashire

1937

Elsie waited and waited and then she waited some more. Cook had kept her secret for her, but Mrs Dawson had worked it out for herself. Elsie was a slight girl and whilst at three to four months of her pregnancy wasn't 'showing', her clothes were pinching. Aprons pulled and her maid's outfit looked stretched on her lithe body. In service, in 1937, staff didn't have enough food to get by on so putting weight on simply didn't happen.

Elsie was sat down on her bed at the top of the house. Cook and Mrs Dawson were sat opposite her in the cramped, unlit bedroom that she called home. Cook, in the gentlest voice that she had, said, "He's not coming back, love. It's been over three months now and you have to make a decision."

Elsie's eyes shone, not with tears but with genuine fear. She knew what life was like for unwed mothers. She would be ostracised, probably by her own family as well as the wider community. She wouldn't be able to get a job; no one would even acknowledge her existence; her life, as far as she was concerned, had ended.

A young Catholic girl with no husband and a baby could be forced into a home if the family saw it that way. Elsie was terrified.

"What should I do?" she asked. Mrs Dawson, forever the pragmatist, laid out the options as she saw them.

"I think you have a choice of three plans of action, none of which are going to be particularly appealing to you. Firstly, you don't have to have it. There are ways to get rid of the baby before it's even born. It costs money, probably money you don't have, but there are methods to stop your pregnancy. It's against the law and it has its risks, but there's someone I know of in Manchester who can help you."

Cook shook her head so violently that the pins fell from her hair and said, "That wouldn't be my first choice, it would be my last. In fact, you could damage yourself so much that you'd be putting your own life at risk." Mrs Dawson looked askance at Cook.

"She has to hear this, Cook. Whether you like it or not, it's one of the girl's options. She doesn't have many, so let her hear."

Elsie, still no tears, just eyes wide open, said, "Please go on, Mrs Dawson. I don't think I could ever do that, what you said, but please continue. It will help to get my head straight. I still can't believe James isn't here to help me with this."

Mrs Dawson did continue.

"He's not one of the options on my list and it would do you good to get him out of your head. You won't be seeing him again. I never trusted those sparkly blue eyes. It was as if he could turn them on and off like a light switch.

"Secondly, I think you could go home. I know you're a Catholic, but your parents may well surprise you and help you out. You would be amazed how many children around here turn out to be grandchildren in the reckoning. Once the lord and lady know you're in the family way, they won't have a job for you.

"Thirdly, there's a home for single girls who are like you in Blackburn. Now, I'm not saying it's particularly pleasant, but you can go there to have the baby while you decide what to do. Then, if it suits you, you can leave it there and get on with your life. They will find some poor couple who couldn't have their own babies and you look for a new job and start again. Or you can stay there and work and bring the baby up yourself."

To Elsie's ears, they didn't sound like choices but different methods of how to die. The third option was the workhouse and once in there the road back to a normal life was a dead end. Nobody wanted to die but everyone did. Cook then spoke up again.

"If you make a quick decision, there's the bonus of no one here, apart from us two, finding out your condition. You will just be a girl who'd had enough of her job and gone back home. The Shuttleworths won't employ you again, but Mrs Dawson can always give a reference."

Mrs Dawson postponed that decision by saying, "We can cross that bridge should we ever come to it. It's your choice, Elsie. No one can make it for you. You've had your fun and now you have to face the consequences."

Elsie knew that if her mother had been sat where Mrs Dawson was sat, she would say exactly the same thing.

She composed herself. For one so young with such a life-changing, difficult decision to make, she knew that she couldn't rush this choice. The thought of raising a baby as her own in the society she lived in was beyond the realms of the world she knew. She also believed that she couldn't kill the baby because to her that's what the abortion would be. She therefore pretty much knew what option she was going to have to take. When faced with no choice at all, she did what she had been brought up to believe: you accepted the situation and kept fighting.

Her next question sealed her fate.

"Where is this home in Blackburn and how much money will I need?"

Elsie was not wearing the engagement ring that James had presented to her, but it was hidden away at the back of the cistern of the bathroom that she shared with Dot. It was a 4-foot- square hole with a toilet and sink. She wasn't sure what the ring was worth, but the pawnbroker in Burnley town centre had given her £15 for it and she wasn't in a position to turn that down. For her, that was the best part of three months' wages, but she did get her keep as well. It would mean she had something in her purse when she got to Blackburn.

The United Kingdom in 1937 was no place for a single girl carrying a baby. Mrs Dawson, in her act of hard love, had summarised the choices that Elsie had available to her. Many women gave up their children for adoption, unimaginable today, for the simple reason that they were single mothers. Elsie was one of an estimated half a million or more between the '40s and '70s who were marginalised by society, who vindicated their behaviour by wearing their 'respectability' as a badge of honour, who, for whatever their personal reasons, stigmatised illegitimacy.

With access to housing denied them and little family support, even familial hostility, bullied by religious groups or 'support workers', Elsie and thousands like her were almost forced to give up their babies for adoption. Just because they were single parents. Elsie had no information about housing and no financial help, excusing the pawned engagement ring given to her by her lover who himself had some explaining to do. Elsie had no idea what kind of a mother she would be or could be, but society was about to brand her as unfit; she was going to be prevented from becoming a mother at all.

Coming from a Catholic family exacerbated the situation for Elsie. She knew that if her strong Catholic father found out she was pregnant, 'the disgrace would kill him'. Elsie was left with the choice of attending the Catholic home in Blackburn and then giving the baby up for adoption.

It didn't take her very long to pack. Cook had given her some old cleaning clothes of her own that as she got bigger would at least give her something to wear. *Shabby but clean*; *something I need to get used to*, thought Elsie. She arrived with a small cardboard suitcase, and she left with a small cardboard suitcase. Everything in the world she had was in there.

She left on Friday, 14th May 1937 with little fanfare. Most of the household had guessed her condition, five and a half months pregnant, she believed, but only Cook and Mrs Dawson knew for sure. Cook had organised a collection for her that came to one shilling and ninepence and would at least pay for her train journey to Blackburn. Dot walked with her to the railway station. The daffy girl still couldn't understand why Elsie was going; she thought she was just heartbroken after the disappearance of James. Elsie was shaken up over no contact but Dot, even though she shared a bedroom with Elsie, was as innocent as a bluebell in the snow and didn't know she was with child.

It was a forty-five-minute walk to Rose Grove Station and for every step of the way Dot either snivelled or cried. On a couple of occasions, she actually bawled, attracting the attention of several bystanders. Elsie just smiled and nodded, indicating she had everything under control. She hadn't cried when saying goodbye to Mr Dawson and Mrs Dawson, no relation, to Cook and the other maids. The lads in the garden hadn't even noticed she was missing. It was a tough life and it 'didn't do' to get too attached to anyone in a working environment. Somebody needed to tell that to Dot as she cried as though her whole family had been sent off to the impending war.

Eventually, they arrived at the tiny brick station that was Rose Grove. The station had been in existence since 1848 and had been built with novel low-lying platforms to allow easier access to the train carriages. It wasn't a particularly busy station, but many trains went through every day on what used to be the Lancashire and Yorkshire Railway before it merged in 1923 into the London, Midland and Scottish Railway, a name that did not go down well in both Lancashire and Yorkshire. Elsie had a fifteen-minute wait before pulling herself into the carriage and leaving a sobbing mess of a Dot on the platform edge.

"Don't worry, Dot. I'll come and see you when I get straight. I just have one or two decisions to make and when I'm set in Blackburn perhaps you can come and see me as well if Mrs Dawson will let you." Dot could not get her words out and just wailed and waved a sodden wet mess that had started the day as a lady's handkerchief but now looked like a dishcloth.

"I'm only thirty or forty minutes away. I'll write and send my address when I find somewhere."

This time, Dot managed to speak.

"But I can't read very well." The last word elongated and turned into a howl. *Weeeeelllll.* Elsie wondered if Dot had any more tears in her. The train pulled away from the platform and the two friends waved at each other, Elsie too found something sticking in her throat slightly but held it together. The two friends never met again.

Elsie shared a carriage with what looked like two railroad men, an older lady and a mother with a little boy, who were sat facing her by the window. She smiled at them all in turn but only the mother smiled back. That would be whom Elsie concentrated her conversation on.

"How old is he?"

"He's coming up to four now. Should be in school today but I'm taking him to the hospital in Blackburn." And that was that. For the next forty minutes, the young mother, who looked closer in age to Dot than she did to Elsie, told of her child's ailments and how her own doctor didn't 'have a clue' what was wrong with him. He was sneezing some days, coughing others. 'You should see the muck he's bringing up.' The lad's legs didn't seem long enough for his body, and he hardly spoke unless it was to their dog.

"To be honest with yer, he's a right miserable little bugger most of the time. But I do love him." And as if to prove her love she ruffled his hair, causing him to pull away from her, resulting in a belt round the back of the head.

"Don't pull away when I'm trying to love yer." Even under her own difficult circumstances, Elsie had to smile. The train continued to trundle on its tracks, rocking so much that it felt like being on a boat. Through Huncoat, then the big town of Accrington, lots of activity there, Church then Rishton, before finally rocking into Blackburn Station. It was 11.30am on Friday, the 14th of May 1937, and Elsie had the rest of her life in front of her.

Blackburn had been around since 1086 and was mentioned in the Domesday Book as 'Blachebourne'. By 1911, the closest recorded census to Elsie's train pulling into the station, Blackburn had grown to over 130,000 people, a number from which it would only decline. For the first half of the twentieth century, it was famous and world renowned for its cotton industry, with over 90,000 looms in operation at its peak in the town. In 1933, Japan started twenty-four-hour round-the-clock cotton production and soon became the largest cotton producer in the world. In 1937, the town mills were still producing cotton on 37,000 looms, but the decline since the Great War had been dramatic, with seventy-four mills closing in less than four years. The threat of World War II would offer some reprieve as cotton was needed for the war effort, but there was no denying there was 'trouble at mill'.

Elsie wasn't oblivious to this and knew that her chances of work would be severely limited as the cotton decline had been widely discussed in the region since she could remember. She was heading for the Blackburn Christian United Workhouse even though its name had changed to the King's Park Institution ten years earlier. Cook still knew it as the 'Workhouse' and that was that. Little did Elsie know but her unborn baby was going to be taken from her two days after birth and given to a more rewarding family. 'Better for the child and the mother'.

It was a mile-and-a-half walk to Haslingden Road and the institution premises. Elsie wasn't too sure whether the word institution was more daunting than workhouse. At least she understood the terminology of a workhouse, whereas an institution to her mind conjured up images of people locked away in padded cells. She had no option. Squinting into and against the light late spring rain, she squelched her way to the home. That's the word she would think of: home. It left her feeling less worried. The building that loomed into view couldn't have been less like the definition of 'home'.

King's Park Institution sprawled over several acres of land and included four prominent outcrops of building standing proudly against the horizon, like the four horsemen of the apocalypse. The buildings were topped with rounded turrets sharpening into points that pricked at the sky like a Hanoverian castle, and one even had a straight industrial chimney that reached upwards to the building's highest point. The bases of the building were impossible to see from a distance as they were cloaked with a thick industrial brick wall, keeping everyone out or everyone in. It couldn't have looked less like a place for desperate young mothers had there been a moat and pulled drawbridge with archers spread evenly across the forbidding outer walls.

Originally, the entrance to the workhouse was to the north of the building but when Elsie arrived it had been split into male accommodation to the west of the premises, while she had to set off into the rain coming in from the east to find her entrance. After standing in the rain for several more minutes, she was met at the entrance by Sister Kiara, fresh off the boat from Ireland. She looked no older than Elsie was herself but, in fact, was a good ten years older. Kiara originally meant 'dark-haired', but no one would ever know as there wasn't a hair on show, pulled back so severely and hidden beneath the black veil and white cap, known as a 'coif'.

Sister Kiara was all business.

"I assume you are with child and unmarried or you wouldn't be here. If you wish to stay and have your baby, there are forms to fill in and legal documents to sign. We will help you if you help yourself, with God's blessing. Let's start with the easy questions. Your name, please?" Too startled to lie and too naïve to have a story ready, Elsie told the truth.

"Elsie Scott."

"Address?"

"I don't have an address. I was most recently in service in a house in Burnley, but it wasn't my home. I guess I don't have a home now, I'm... I'm..."

"Homeless," breezed the efficient Sister Kiara. "Well, with God willing, you will be able to call here your home for the next few months. But you must know you will work hard, very hard. But no harder than all of us, those of us blessed by God and those of us who are yet to be blessed by God."

"Of-of-of course," stammered Elsie. She had expected this, had been warned about the matter-of-fact approach by the Catholic nuns, but knowing about something and dealing with it are two very different sides of a bent penny. She had to admit she was getting herself flustered and wondering if moving into the workhouse was the right course of action for her.

"What, if anything, was your previous employment?"

"I was a maid. In service, I told you. Not far away at Gawthorpe Manor. Mrs Dawson, the housekeeper, said she would supply me with a reference, should I be—"

"You won't need any reference here. Are you Catholic?"

"Yes, I am. Baptised at St Theresa's..." and for the first time, Elsie changed her story "...St Theresa's, Wigan." She decided she couldn't tell the nun her full story just in case any follow-up happened and word got back to her family, although, in 1937, the only way would be by letter, and Elsie had never given her full home address to anyone. Even Gawthorpe Manor weren't that interested.

After a few more questions such as date of birth, next of kin, how many months pregnant she was, Sister Kiara stopped, smiled winningly and said, "That's it, you're all done."

"So, I'm in?" asked the expectant Elsie.

"I don't think there'll be any problems but if you come back here this time tomorrow, I'll have an answer for you. The Mother Superior Mary Madonna makes all the final decisions, and she will do so after evening prayers."

"But where will I go? What will I do? I know no one in the town and have nowhere to stay."

Sister Kiara was ready for the question, having been here many times before.

"Go back the way you came up Haslingden Road. Take a right into Bennington Street and first left into Crossfield Street. Number twenty-seven is a women's hostel house run by Mrs Staples. She will charge slightly over the normal price, but you will be provided with a relatively clean bed, or at least a dry bed, and a morning meal of varied quality, but you may be lucky. One piece of advice, keep your shoes on.

"See you tomorrow and may God keep you safe." With her final comment, the nun rose and with a wave of her arm showed Elsie back out the way she had come in. The large key chain jangled from her habit as every door seemed to be locked, even to the vestibule at the forefront of the institute.

"Peace be with you, my child," and she was gone, and Elsie was once again stood outside and open to the elements, albeit the rain had ceased temporarily. Staying brave, she moved on, following the directions given. She didn't exactly remember the first street name but after asking an old lady for directions found herself on Crossfield Street.

The street was rows of white stone terraced cottages lined up on either side of a dirt track road but at least with a pavement to walk on either side. The original white stone had turned a grubby brown but still the cottages had a certain charm about them. Dirty children played in the gutters and many front doors were cast open but blocked with women of all shapes and sizes wearing aprons with their hair hidden by tightly bound headscarves. Most had cigarettes hanging from their mouths.

As Elsie walked past them, they stopped their conversations and some even had throwaway comments to make.

"Here's another one for Staples."

"She's well gone, already showing."

Some were far coarser. "Should have kept yer knickers on, love."

"I'll bet yer keep yer legs closer together next time."

Elsie would not dignify their catcalls by responding, but it was a walk of shame she wished she didn't have to take. Her own self-hatred did not need any more petrol thrown on it to keep it alight.

Some comments were more conciliatory. "Leave her alone, poor kid. Us women should be sticking together. It's the bloody men not the young girls that's the problem, and they just swan off into the night and don't give a fu..." Her rant was called short by her neighbour.

"Mildred, watch yer mouth. Kids are playing out. Look at our Fred covered in mud. Little bastard."

By the time Elsie had walked the street to number twenty-seven, it felt like three miles, but she wasn't left long on the doorstep. It was one of the few houses that had its door closed and it was painted white when most of the doors held a far darker colour.

"Come in, love, before the Crossfield Coven get yer." Elsie did as she was told. Mrs Staples must be 'doing well for herself', as she was the size of a small outhouse. She didn't look fat to Elsie, but she was solid. She remembered something her dad used to say: 'Five-foot-eight-square'. Thick muscle-bound arms protruded from a short-sleeve blouse, with the sleeves so tight on the arms they looked like string around a cut of meat. Mrs Staples was not a lady to take for granted.

"This is how it is. Two and six in advance for a bed for the night and a hot meal tomorrow morning. No visitors allowed; men, women or children. I'm not against men, I'm against everyone. I won't bother you if you don't bother me. You'll be in a room with four other girls. It's a bit cramped but it's first come, first served on the beds. There is a bathroom at the end of the landing but only cold water. I assume you're up at the workhouse, so it'll be one night for you. That'll be five shillings, please."

"But I'm only staying one night."

"Minimum stay two nights. If you don't like it, there's plenty out there who will."

Elsie scrambled in her purse and took out the right money even though she knew you could find places to sleep for ten shillings for the whole week. She flashed a few notes that she'd received for the pawned engagement ring. She dropped the coins into the large mitt that was Mrs Staples's hand.

"Word of advice, love. Keep that purse tight to your body when you go to sleep. Probably best down yer knickers. Trust me. If you don't, it won't be there in the morning. Follow me and I'll show you where you're going."

Elsie followed the broad back up a narrow flight of stairs and into a back bedroom. There were two beds in both far corners of the room and three mattresses strewn haphazardly across the floor. There were no sheets on any of the beds. Elsie was handed a raggedy, stained blue horsehair blanket that was so coarse it could have been used to scour the bath.

"Give this back when you leave or that's another two shillings from your purse. Take the choice of your mattress. The beds are regulars, and they won't take kindly to a stranger landing up in there. Look after yourself, love." And Mrs Staples was gone.

Elsie took a look around at her place of rest for the next night. She prayed to all the gods, not only the one she had been brought up to worship, that it wouldn't be any longer than that even though she'd had to pay for more. If this was a clean bed for the night, she could call herself fortunate she hadn't fallen on a dirty one.

The room may be being used as a bedroom but must once have been a storage room as where there was any floor space not taken by a bed or a mattress, there were boxes of all descriptions. Some with yellow or green mould as an added embellishment. Rags and dusters spilled out of some, while others held brass candlesticks and crumpled-up newspapers. By the condition of each box, they had been thoroughly examined for anything of any value. An old sideboard was up against one wall, with misshapen and broken drawers jutting out like ill-fitting teeth in a tramp's mouth. There was one small window, nailed closed, with an old tea towel tacked over it to provide a curtain that watered the sunlight down into a dreamlike state. A head peered over the top of a pile of rags on one bed. It belonged to a lady on in years, and her grey hair pirouetted around her head like fine spider gossamer.

She looked at Elsie, literally looked her up and down, before yawning, farting and turning over to face the wall. The wall that in all corners of the room had mottled wallpaper falling down from the top, like dog ears heavy with speckled green spots of damp. The wallpaper was some kind of flock and looked to be from the previous century. Finally, the smell reminded Elsie of the rabbits that her dad kept in the backyard back home.

There was a bathroom of sorts that did have running water; not all these houses had water both down and upstairs. There was no flushing toilet. A slop bucket, luckily recently emptied, provided the latrine function. Elsie decided she had to get out but by doing so she would not be able to stake claim to the second bed or even one of the better mattresses; two were shedding their contents like a dandelion loses its seeds. She took her belongings and found Mrs Staples, saying she would be back later for bed.

"No later than nine, though, or you won't get in. And I don't care what's happening on the other side of this door, it stays shut after nine. If you want the decent mattress, I'd make it seven if I was you. I have two regulars up there who don't move most days, so choice is limited."

Elsie spent the rest of the day walking the streets of Blackburn. She did find a little café where she treated herself to tea, a sandwich and an Eccles cake, and she stayed until they showed her the door as she was taking up a table. And that 'meant money'. When the rain started to come down again, but harder this time, she made her way back to Crossfield Street. It would have been easy to start feeling sorry for herself, but Elsie Scott was made of 'stern stuff' and refused to get too down. Her 'digs' for the night were dreadful and no place to bring a baby into the world, but it was one night, perhaps two, if she could get into the Catholic institution.

Back at the 'women's hostel', as Sister Kiara had kindly

called twenty-seven Crossfield Street, Elsie grabbed herself the second-best mattress, as a young girl had taken the one she wanted. The girl was also wrapped in Elsie's blue blanket as well as her own and that took ten minutes of arguing and fighting before Elsie snatched it roughly from the girl's grasp, who spat viciously at Elsie, but her aim was wide. Was there no one in this hellhole who behaved with some form of civility?

Elsie slept spasmodically, for the most part curled up into a foetus, in accord with her own child curled up inside her. Her dreams were vivid and strange, and she murmured through the night to shouts of, "Shut your cakehole, you silly bitch," and other such encouraging words.

Light came early through the towelling and Elsie didn't wait about. Yesterday, she had spent so long in the café because at least she could use their facilities, but now she wanted to be first in the 'bathroom'. Toilet complete, and her gag reflex fully tested, she threw freezing water over herself to firstly clean the stench of the place off her and secondly to wake her up to the trials of the day ahead. She was first downstairs and sat at the large kitchen table that had last been wiped down some time before Christmas 1935.

Breakfast was edible, just. Watery eggs and burnt crispy bacon and stale bread. Elsie was very hungry and ate everything she was offered. Other women and girls sat and joined her at the table at different parts of her meal. She counted eight in all, which meant there had to be other rooms in the house also full of stinking beds and mattresses.

"Will you be back tonight, love?" asked Mrs Staples, thinking if not she could sell the space twice over. Even in her line of business, it was all about the margins.

"I honestly don't know, Mrs Staples. I have to go back to the institution to see if they will accept me."

"Oh, you'll be all right there. They'll take anyone who they can turn into another slave. You do know, don't you, that they run an industrial laundry out of that place. They'll have you slaving until you drop your load and then they'll sell your baby and chuck you out unless you want to keep working there. Yer better off here with us lot."

The women around the table were either disinterested or nodded agreeably. There were no dissenting voices when Mrs Staples spoke.

"Well, I need somewhere to have my baby so, like it or not, that's my lot. Goodbye and thank you." Elsie's mum, Lily Scott, had drilled into all her children, always, always, keep your manners. And Elsie still wanted to make her mum proud. She handed her blanket back to Mrs Staples and, nodding her short-lived landlady a goodbye, left the room and then the house without another word.

Her second walk of shame was not as intimidating as her previous one had been. Several houses that had been shut up for the night were yet to raise their shutters, like droopy eyelids still sticky with sleep. Yesterday, as Elsie had been walking around the town, she noted the Co-op Emporium library in Town Hall Street but had also noted the queues to get into the building. It was an impressive large stone building, resembling more a church than a library, with a vaulted double-fronted façade and high arched stained glass windows and an imposing arched doorway. Elsie wanted to get there before the queues started to build up.

She was there at 7.40am and had to wait until nine for

entry but she was the first and, grabbing the *Daily Mirror*, she snuggled herself away at the rear of the quiet room next to a window providing ample light to read by. She had only left Gawthorpe Manor less than twenty-four hours ago, but it felt so long that she thought her baby must be due. Looking down at the paper, she realised she had picked up Thursday's copy. The headlines in the paper on Thursday, 13th May 1937 read:

'The Crowning of George VI King and Emperor'

The photograph beneath was a poor one showing the back of the Archbishop raising the crown above the new king's head, but his gowns fell in front of the king so the photographer had managed to erase both the faces of the two people he was trying to capture.

It almost seemed impossible to fathom but with all her internal problems she had forgotten, missed or simply not cared that the wider world was still spinning, and one of the greatest royal stories of all time had been unfurling in the past months. Earlier that week, King George VI and Queen Elizabeth had been crowned king and queen at the coronation ceremony at Westminster Abbey. This was after his brother, Edward VIII, had abdicated last December because he could not marry the woman he loved, Wallis Simpson. Elsie's eyes filled with tears at the lengths some men would go to, in order to be with the woman they loved. Whereas for her the previous December had left her alone with a very different present.

She spent most of the morning reading from the daily papers provided free in the public library. She also noted the empty shelves around her. In the depression between the wars, the UK public libraries were a place of solace, warmth and companionship, and books were borrowed at a previously unseen unprecedented rate. Elsie wasn't in the mood for company and after reading most of the newspapers, dominated by the coronation, she treated herself to the first few chapters of a borrowed copy of *Jayne Eyre* before replacing it on the shelf, gathering herself for the storm ahead and leaving the library, with great trepidation for the institution, aptly for the times called King's.

Another thirty-minute walk and Elsie was back at the eastern doors of King's Park Institution, where Sister Kiara had some news for her. Elsie would reserve judgement as to whether it was good or unwelcome news.

"Sister Superior Mary Madonna has blessed you and with God's wishes you are welcome to stay at the institute until such time we feel you are ready to go back to the world outside." Elsie didn't notice the nuances of what she had been told but, essentially, she was handing over the running of her life to the sisters of Saint John the Baptist. While the Catholic Church didn't have the power in England that it possessed in Ireland, she was nevertheless taking a risk with the raising of her unborn child.

Once she was accepted into the institute, Elsie adapted far better than most to the stringent rules, challenging work and access to the outside world that many others suffered intensely with. She was genuinely grateful for the opportunity to get off the street, away from her family, to have some order to her existence and rules to her life. At times, she saw it as no more demanding than her months in service had been. Her only concerns were for her child and what would become of it and the deception to her family. They thought she was still at the Manor and as neither side ever wrote that often would continue to believe so.

The summer of 1937 was not a particularly memorable one in terms of the weather. June was mostly wet; July was wetter, with thunderstorms, and the summer broke out for one month in August and the north-west received some sun. This suited Elsie perfectly as she was getting bigger, and her time was drawing near. The sleeping arrangements were as one may expect in a hospital and the dormitories were long and narrow and slept many young girls. Most of the 'inmates' were either pregnant, had lost a child or had recently had a child that had been taken away from the new mother and 'adopted' by 'acceptable' middle-class families.

As September dawned, Elsie had taken on the late pregnancy waddle as her preferred walking gait and was finding it increasingly difficult to manufacture the cotton clothes that the institute made to help raise funds for their meagre existence. The girls, for producing as many garments as a hundred per week, got their bed and board as payment. Elsie still had the majority of the funds she had received from the pawnshop that she had managed to smuggle in the ripped lining of her cardboard suitcase. 'Lily Scott never raised no fools'.

She had made friends with a young girl from Yorkshire – she wouldn't be more exact than that – who was due about a month later than Elsie. She called herself Dolly, but Elsie thought this was not her real name as she was only fourteen years old. Dolly knew what she wanted. She wasn't bothered about keeping her child.

"I just want to get shut and get back to farm," became her mantra over the months that Elsie knew her. She also wouldn't comment about the father and could get physically threatening if pushed on the matter. Elsie believed Dolly hadn't even known what she was doing when she conceived, and her reticence to hold back on the father's name could be because he was closer to home than she cared to think about. Even so, Elsie became good friends with the girl, whose bed was right next to Elsie's in the dormitory.

At night, they shared secrets they were prepared to share. Not everything, but they both needed someone to talk to in the situation they found themselves. Elsie enjoyed the fact that the girl was indeed just a girl, and she could be the wiser, older and more mature partner in the friendship, not so far removed from her friendship with Dot back at the Manor. She liked the thought that Dolly would come to her for advice and help. It made her relevant and visible, if not to others then certainly to herself.

She did share with Dolly that she wasn't sure yet if she would actually give her baby up for adoption, putting on a stronger and braver manner than she felt. She knew, just like everyone else in the home, that she had signed away her rights to keep her own child. Plus, the girls never saw outside the home, hospital, institution or, to use the word most commonly used by the girls, prison. Every door had a key and was invariably locked, so you could always hear when a Baptist sister, shorthand for St John the Baptist sister, came jangling into the room or down a corridor.

Now that Elsie was in her final weeks, she was asked to make clothes for her own baby. The cruelty of having to make a leaving outfit for your own child as it was taken from your breast against your will and 'sold' for a donation to the institute.

"We don't want your child looking like it's not cared for when it goes," echoed the mantra from the sisters. On the 6th of September, Elsie went into labour. She was cleaning the entrance hall and the back of the staircase with a large bucket of dirty water and a mop when her waters broke.

"When you've finished with the baby, you can come back and finish cleaning what you started. No one else will want to clean up your mess," were the encouraging words from Sister Michael. If there was a tougher bride of Jesus than Michael, Elsie didn't want to meet her. It was a complicated birth, needing the use of forceps and numerous attempts to 'turn' the baby. Elsie lost a lot of blood over the twenty-four hours, but she was strong and with a final push and scream, which was probably heard back in Burnley, a baby boy came crying into the world at eleven of the morning on Tuesday the 7th of September 1937.

She was tired but still had her faculties and Elsie exclaimed, making sure that everyone heard, "He's to be called James Harold Scott, after his father and my grandfather. Let you all be a witness to this," she said to the nuns and midwife who were in the birthing room. "I don't want you changing his name when I'm not around. It's James Harold Scott as God is my witness, and you must all hark God's word."

"Silence, girl," said Sister Marina, who had helped deliver the baby boy. "You don't have a say in the child's name. It's for the parents to decide what he's to be called." That was when the helplessness of her situation truly hit Elsie for the first time. She would feed the baby later today but then that would be the end of her involvement in his life. He would be handed over to new parents, arriving on Friday the 10th of September at the latest, so they could start their new lives with a pleasant weekend.

Elsie, exhausted, holding her as yet unwashed child, feeling the connection, parts of her own body still clinging to his puckered skin, knew she would not be able to give him up. She had seen his bright blue eyes, so much like her own, and the advice of the nuns to not form a bond and not to breastfeed him were already too late. How ironic that the only brides in the room, the brides of Christ, would be the only ones not to bring life into the world. Yet, Elsie, not a bride and with no prospect now of ever being one, pulsed with the new life she had introduced as James Harold. In her fatigue, Elsie's mind started to plan.

Next day and Elsie and Dolly were talking in hurried whispers at morning prayers.

"You'll never get away with it," said Dolly. Then, after a moment's thought, "Never mind you, I'll never get away with it."

"But will you try, for me? I can't give James over for adoption. I know I signed the papers, but they can't have him. They had no right to get me to sign when I was weak and vulnerable. They just use us to help fund their prison. Just because I've committed a 'mortal sin' and in the eyes of the Catholic Church I'll never go to heaven. Who thinks up such wicked rules?

"All I want you to do is pretend to be ill, but it will have to be tomorrow, after supper. If you can call that grey mess they serve us supper. When we come back to the dormitory, it's the young nun who brings us back. She's only been here a fortnight. We know the rules better than she does. But you have to be good."

"Don't worry. I know exactly what I'm going to do. Poor Sister Audrey won't know what's hit her. When we get back tomorrow night, you call her over. Today, put your stuff in the cleaning cupboard on the ground floor, by the stairs. The nuns don't go in there anyway."

"I'll take things one at a time. I'll wear extra layers then as I'm going about my cleaning duties, I'll strip a layer off and pop things in there," replied Elsie.

"What about your suitcase?"

"I'll put all the baby clothes in now and take it downstairs straight away. If anyone stops me, I'll show them what's in the case and say I'm just taking them to the nursery for James and his new parents."

"You're not as daft as you look, are you?" laughed Dolly. "Come on, let's go and get some layers on ready for tomorrow. There's only me and you goes in that bloody cleaning cupboard anyway."

For the rest of the day, Elsie and Dolly transferred the majority of Elsie's belongings, of which there was very little, to the cleaning cupboard. The most important was the suitcase, not because it held all of Elsie's, and now James's, whole belongings but also because the money that Elsie received for her pawned engagement ring was tucked away in there. Elsie didn't feel all that well after the birth, but she had to keep going. If she didn't, she would lose James forever. She was still losing blood but at a trickle now, not much worse than a heavy period. She was tough because she had to be.

Thursday was traumatic. The nuns took James away. He would spend the rest of his time now in the nursery, so the mother/son bond did not grow any stronger. Elsie was playing the distraught mother, but it didn't need much playing as she knew if her and Dolly's plan failed then this was no act from a play. The day dragged. Elsie begged to see her son one last time but was told 'no', and 'it was for her own good'. The Sisters of St John the Baptist had left the word 'compassion' out of their vows.

Elsie was sewing. Dolly cleaning in the kitchen. They had little chance to speak during the day, but the stage was set, and Dolly intended to give an award-winning performance as 'Girl in background with stomach problems'. Even Elsie didn't know what Dolly had in mind.

"It'll just make it look more believable if you look shocked as well." *Shocked*, thought Elsie, *what is the daft Yorkshire girl going to do? But if it works, I don't care*. Elsie was starting to realise that it was a totally unnatural experience to carry a child for nine months only for it to be snatched away at the moment of birth. She was determined to do everything she could to stop it from happening.

The day wore on and so did Elsie's nerves until she had imagined every possible outcome to the course of events she was about to instigate. Dolly, on the other hand, was relishing her part and was giddy with excitement. To their knowledge, no one had ever 'escaped' with their own baby before. Certainly, there were no stories of anyone having done so.

No one had ever escaped because no one had ever even tried before, such was the stranglehold held by the sisters over the mostly very young girls 'welcomed' to the institution.

Suppertime came. A grey oat gruel made with water and not milk was the normal evening fare, and Thursday, the 9th of September was not going to be any different. The clock chimed six o'clock and the women of King's Park made their way to the dining hall. After hours of crying and moaning, Elsie had been allowed to give James his last feed. His last feed from her breast if the plan failed. Dolly and Elsie chose to sit apart. In fact, Dolly feigned a slight of some description and sat away from the others. Only by one or two places but enough to be on her own. The gruel came and, if you were lucky, you got a dab of raspberry jam, made in the institution by three of the nuns, on the top.

By six-thirty, the women had been marched back to their dormitories. Sister Audrey led the group of which Elsie and Dolly were members. Some of the women, mostly pregnant, were silent, but some joked and fooled around just like any group of friends would do. Elsie's face had gone the same colour as the gruel she had been unable to eat. Even before they had reached their own cots, Dolly collapsed in a heap on the floor. Sister Audrey was responsible for all fourteen of the girls in her dormitory and as the newest member of the John the Baptists, had never had anyone take ill on her before.

Dolly was giving it all she was worth. Rolling on the floor, clutching her swollen abdomen, she never screamed or shouted but moaned in a tone not dissimilar to Frankenstein's monster in the Boris Karloff film. The moaning got louder, and the writhing became worse. Sister Audrey knelt next to her, but Dolly was face down on the floor and commenced banging her head on the wooden floorboards. If Elsie hadn't known the plan, she would herself have believed that there was something dramatically wrong with her young friend.

And then Dolly produced the coup de grâce. She had been sat on her own at supper, so no one had noticed what she was doing. She turned away from the floor and faced Sister Audrey. Her eyes were popping out of her head and her face looked badly swollen. Swollen for but a second as a grey and red mess erupted from her mouth like an exploding bottle of beer that has been brewed for too long. The filthy, red semi-liquidised gruel and jam landed full in the face of Sister Audrey and dripped and crawled down her habit like a slug taking a walk. Dolly emitted a gasp and then a scream that had some of the other girls crying themselves. Dolly grabbed the sick-strewn habit of Sister Audrey and with gruel-flecked spit flying from her mouth yelled, "Don't leave me. Something is wrong with my baby." Dolly had held in her mouth as much gruel and jam as she possibly could for over thirty minutes before spewing the whole lot into the unsuspecting face of the wide-eyed nun. Dolly grabbed Sister Audrey with the strength of a mother lifting a car to save their own child.

"DO NOT GO, Sister," she shouted. Elsie stepped forward and spoke.

"Sister Audrey, you must stay with her. If she dies or the baby dies, you will be held responsible for leaving her on her own. Give me your keys and I'll go for help." Sister Audrey did not hesitate as Dolly groaned as if she was giving birth to the Antichrist. She unhooked her keys from her habit and passed them to Elsie. Elsie and Dolly looked at each other and said goodbye with their eyes. At this point, not only had they managed to trick Sister Audrey but most of the young women also.

Elsie took the keys and ran. The door to their dorm was still unlocked so no issue there, but there was an iron door with bars that blocked the staircase. Elsie had no idea which key did which, and there were at least eight keys on the heavy iron ring that they jangled off. She had to keep her cool and be methodical. At this point, she had every reason to be dashing around with the keys as she was going for help but knew only too well that if she bumped into another sister, the keys would be taken from her. She started with one key and moved around the chain until the door clicked open. It was her fourth attempt. She took the time to lock the door behind her, thinking that at some point Sister Audrey would come looking for her. She intended to be down the road by then. She didn't know that fate would step in and that would not be the case.

Next stop was the nursery for James. There was always someone watching the babies, and this was as far as her plan had been imagined. From now on in, it was her wits versus the sisters. Through another landing door on the second floor, locked again behind her, and she was stood outside the nursery. Apart from James, there were two other babies in there that she knew of so there would have to be a nurse or sister. Putting the keys away, she banged on the door. No answer. She tried the door. It was unlocked.

Why would it be locked? she thought. The oldest sister in the building was sat at the desk. She hadn't heard Elsie banging on the door. No one knew for sure how old Sister Agatha was but in her nineties was the best guess of the women. If there was a Christian God looking down on Elsie, He was on her side. Agatha, God bless her, should have been in a home herself, not looking after newborns, thought Elsie. A debate for another day. Elsie walked over to another baby, picked him or her up – hard to tell, she thought – walked over to Sister Agatha and gave her the baby, saying, "Look after him."

She then went over to James, the sleeping James, and picked him up and marched straight out again as if she ruled the world. Agatha sat with her mouth open, knowing she needed to sound some form of alarm, but she could only get out of the chair on her own by taking her time and pulling herself upright. She had a baby in her hands. Elsie was on the run again now, knowing she was running out of time. One thing in her favour was that all the stairway doors used the same key, so she wasn't having to trial and error all the time. Especially now she was carrying James.

She was on the ground floor and could now hear some form of commotion above her. Grabbing her case from the cleaning cupboard, and her money, she made her way to the inside door of the vestibule on the other side of which stood the impressive front door of the wing. She tried every key but couldn't get through. She was hyperventilating now and, placing James by her feet on the floor, tried the keys again, realising she had missed one. The large half wood, half glass door turned inwards. Picking the grizzling baby and her suitcase up, she went into the vestibule. She had no time to lock the door behind her but closed it. Voices behind her echoed off the booming front door and she dropped to the ground as quickly as someone holding a newborn baby could.

James cried. Not loud but unmistakable to anyone who was listening out. Elsie lay across the bottom of the vestibule door, clutching James to her chest like the last life jacket on a sinking ship. The bottom half of the door was thick oak, but the top was hazy glazed glass, like the sort used in bathroom windows. Elsie was now trembling and clearly heard a voice she didn't recognise saying, "You stay here and shout if you see anyone. She can't be far. Sister Audrey doesn't have a key for outside doors." Elsie could have wept, and then she did. The silent tears rolled down her grim face and she tried to contain her sobs. There was nothing she could do apart from hope that she had the front door deadbolt key even after what she had heard.

She silently stood. Directly in front of her through the frosted glass she could make out the dark habit of a nun with her back to her. Elsie turned and commenced running through the keys, but she was done. Her shoulders shook with the strain, and she dropped the keys on the floor. The vestibule door was pushed open and there stood Sister Kiara. Elsie would have to carry the burden of her loss for the rest of her life. She held James to her chest and stoically held her arm out with the suitcase held out. Her last line of defence: a cardboard suitcase.

Sister Kiara looked behind her and then held her finger to her lips. One of the few trustees who had an external key, her role was to welcome newcomers to the institution; she had the key to the front door. To Elsie's utter and complete amazement, she pulled the top and bottom bolts from the door before unshackling a key as large as her palm and turning it in the lock. The door pulled open and Sister Kiara said only one word, "Go," before hustling Elsie out into the twilight air. The last thing Elsie remembered about the institute was the noise of the bolt being pulled back into place as she half ran, half stumbled away into the September evening dusk.

Hong Kong and Home

1960–61

James Holmes, born James Harold Scott, spent the rest of his time in Hong Kong driving for Corporal Tyldesley. He refused to share his news with anyone. He closed up and internalised his feelings. His friends, especially closer friends, namely Jock and Ginger, noted the change in him and did their utmost to open up Rocky, but he lived up to the false nickname he had been given and stayed as closed as a rock. The corporal became as much a friend as was allowed when it came to a 'man with stripes' and someone from the rank and file. But Rocky was a good driver and once his confidence rose, Tyldesley knew he had someone that could be relied upon to deliver on time and with everything in one piece.

Rocky told Ginger and Jock in one of his more verbose moments, "Best job I've ever had, this, lads. Driving around Hong Kong with the corp is about a hundred times better than cutting glass at Pilks. If I just had Liz here with me, I'd be set."

"What about your beloved Saints?" asked Jock. "You wouldn't be able to go and see them every week."

"I know, you're right. I do love Saints but it's funny what you can get used to if you try hard enough, isn't it?" Jock sort of shrugged his shoulders. which Rocky didn't see, as the two were falling asleep late one night when this conversation took place. Moments later, Jock was snoring but Rocky was thinking and wondering what he himself would be able to put up with once he got home.

The eight months in Hong Kong flew by in a blur of trucks, drunken nights out, drilling and the occasional fieldcraft training into the mangroves. Fieldcraft would cover such training as looking after yourself and your equipment, providing food and shelter, moving and observing while remaining hidden, judging distances, patrolling, night manoeuvres, being under enemy fire and using sentries.

Rocky lived for driving his truck and going out on fieldcraft manoeuvres. He adored going out into the mangroves and having to 'play at soldiers' as it was as close as this regiment would ever get to any real action. As Rocky saw it, 'it was all of the fun with none of the threat' and it took his mind away from such existential questions as, 'Who the fuck am I?' Before too long, the squaddies were packing again for the trip home.

The journey home didn't start too well as *HMT Dunera*, or Hired Military Transport *Dunera*, crept into Hong Kong Harbour with its propeller falling off. The *Dunera* was another World War II troop carrier that had been refitted in 1951 and was in the thralls of being refitted again in 1960/61 when the Ministry of Defence decided she was past her sell- buy date.

Nevertheless, this was to be one of her last journeys

before she was indeed sold as a cruise ship. The trip home took six weeks, but the journey was far more pleasant than the journey out had been. This was because the majority of the transformation to a cruise ship had already been completed and on the trip home the troops had six choices of food ("lovely grub this" – Ginger), their very own swimming pool, no real work to undertake and just a 'spot of parading' every morning to count the numbers.

When they landed in Southampton, the men were given six weeks' leave. It was time for Rocky to become James again and to face his demons.

Some of the friendships formed during National Service would last a lifetime.

When James arrived back in St Helens in September 1960, he was in the unenviable position of having to live and love with his in-laws, in a two-up two-down terraced house. He soon realised that Liz had no idea of the contents of the letter he had received from Frank, and he also realised that they would have to start seriously saving for a house. On his second evening home, Liz's mum and dad made themselves scarce by decamping to the local Catholic club, Holy Cross, for a night of bingo and snooker with the Lord's blessing. James took the opportunity to tell the first and most important person to him about his adoption.

Lizzie Holmes was as equally shocked and surprised as James had been. She, however, absorbed the news without experiencing the lingering doubts and sleepless nights when James's mind simply couldn't rest.

"So, what are you going to do?" she asked him. They were sat close together on the small couch facing the television set that took pride of place in the corner of the room, sat on a tall highly polished corner cupboard unit. They held on tight like the last two people on the crashing plane. The coal fire crackled in the grate; no matter the time of year, Lizzie's mum was always cold and claimed that she had never sweated in her life.

"I'm going to do nowt. I need to speak to May and Ken. Frank's away learning how to be a priest. I don't know what I can do. Aunty Elsie is me mum. I haven't thought of anything else for the past few months, but I still haven't come to a conclusion. I don't think I want owt to do with her." James had soon picked up his north-west accent again as though he'd never been away. "What do you think, Liz?"

"I don't know. I haven't had as much time to digest the news as you've had. Part of me is thinking that you've got a mum. The lady you called Mum has been dead a long time now. You've virtually been raised by your May with help from Frank and with as much hindrance as your Ken could supply. How he never killed you, the things you got up to, I'll never know."

"I don't want to see her yet. I need time to think. Apparently, I've got brothers and sisters out there. Look, it's you and me that count. We can't live here with your mum and dad, so first things first. Let me enjoy my time home this time. I've only got eight more months to do and there's rumours flying around that we're going to get out early. National Service has seen its day, I think. When I get home proper, and we have a deposit for a house, I will address meeting me real mum. I'm going to get proper soldier's wages for the next months, not National Servicemen money. What do you say?"

Lizzie, obviously, said yes. They were young and in love and she too wanted to enjoy his time home. They obviously did enjoy their time together as when James became Rocky again for the last stint of his National Service, Graham Holmes was already growing inside Lizzie.

Lizzie, two years junior to James, was working during his leave, learning her skills as a short-hand typist in a local business and so James found himself with time on his hands during the days. He would wander the streets, not wishing to sit in with his in-laws and endless cups of tea but also not wishing to spend any money as he and Lizzie were now working on 'Project Home'.

James was a generous soul and had brought home with him hundreds of cheap cigarettes that he had bought at army prices, knowing that many of his friends and relatives smoked heavily. Having managed to 'pack up' smoking, these he willingly gave away, not even charging what he himself had paid for them; but the endless boredom and walking the town turned him back to the savage weed and, before long, the days turned from clear blue skies into hazy, foggy ones, as he now once again walked with a 'fag' hanging from the corner of his mouth. His mind was always elsewhere as he wrestled with his parental dilemma.

When he returned to Plymouth for the final leg of National Service, he and his returning squaddies found that the barracks were full of young sea cadets. As Ginger said, "How do you bloody double-book a set of barracks?"

The men were shipped off once more but this time to a climate far more in keeping with that they were used to dealing with: the Isle of Wight. Albany Barracks, built in 1798 but called Parkhurst Barracks then, were primitive but adequate. As Jock said, "They've not had a lick of paint since 1800." And another he rolled out: "The murderers, when it's turned into Parkhurst Prison, will have better digs than we do."

It was only for two months but during that time they became darts champions of the local pub, beating all comers due to the fact that some of the lads from Manchester played on a dartboard three quarters the size of the one in the pub. As Rocky said, "They were red-hot," and when the Plough pub challenged the 'Army Boys' to a match, full teams of ten-a-side on Thursday nights, they were set for their two-month stay on the island. The first time Rocky's team arrived, the regulars had put a long banner on the outside of the public house: 'The Plough versus the Army!' The hostelry was full, and food of large pasties and pies was served at half-time and Rocky, Ginger and Jock had never had it so good. Then Plymouth Stonehouse Barracks, originally scheduled for the Lancaster regiment, was freed up again and it was another boat trip, albeit a thirty-minute trip, for the last three months of their service. Only three months because they were to be 'demobbed' in the March of 1961 rather than the June. Rocky was going to leave Plymouth, but it would be James who arrived in St Helens.

Farewells were strong handshakes and manly slaps on the back before Rocky bummed a lift off a squaddie called Hogarth, who was driving all the way to Scotland. Rocky,

Ginger and Jock had one last pint together the night before, and it would be several years before they met up again. Hogarth had a battered Austin 7 that was over twenty years old, and the journey home took over ten hours with stops.

James and Lizzie had been saving hard and, on his arrival, back home, after taking up his old job as a glass cutter, they put a small deposit down and took a mortgage out on a semi-detached house in the Moss Bank area. Lizzie was due in June later that year and James's two years as Rocky, starring in the show of his own life story, was over. He was James Holmes, glass cutter and father-to-be, living in his first home that he could truly call his own, his own and Lizzie's.

During these months, he had been debating his next course of action, but something that May, his sister now cousin, had said to him resonated not only then but for the rest of his life. It was a throwaway comment that May had made when discussing with James the furore caused when Elsie had arrived with him. She said, "What me and Mum thought, James, was, how could a mum abandon their baby?"

Abandon, abandon, abandon. The only word that James heard and the only word that he would hear for the rest of his life. He had been abandoned. His mother had abandoned him. As far as he knew, his father had abandoned him also. *My mum has abandoned me.* Abandon ship – what does that mean? It means leave the ship as you know it's going to sink, and all is lost. He looked up the definition of abandon in a couple of dictionaries.

Abandon – cease to support or look after (someone); desert: or another version – Abandon – give up completely (a practice or a course of action).

His mother had chosen to stop supporting him; his mother had chosen to stop looking after him; his mother had deserted him; his mother had completely given up on him.

James wondered what Rocky might do, as though James and Rocky were two different people. What would his mates, Ginger and Jock back in the army, have said to him? He asked Lizzie what she thought. Not often, just the once. She told him it was up to him, whatever he wanted. As long as she had James, and he was happy, then that's all that concerned her. James made his decision; if his birth mother had abandoned him then he would abandon her, and anything to do with her.

He chose not to see her; he chose to never speak to her; he chose to never see any of his half-siblings. If he bumped into them in the small town, he would be civil, nothing more. For the rest of his life, James Holmes would live as though he had never been adopted. He chose his deceased parents as his true parents and Ken, May and Frank as his siblings. Unless he bumped into her in the street, he would live as though she had never existed. James made his choice and never wavered.

Croydon, London

April Onwards, 1937

"Elsie? Who in the name of God is Elsie? That doesn't matter for now. You're awake. Thank God." The lady sitting at the end of James Knowles's hospital bed started weeping and the young boy next to her grabbed her arm for comfort. He wasn't used to seeing his mother cry, and all she had done since forever, or at least Christmas, was cry, and cry. Regaining her composure, she said, "Doctor, we need the doctor. Wait here with your father, Michael. I won't be long." The boy grabbed at her coat as she left, but she was too quick for him and in a flurry of skirt and stockings she was gone.

The small room had little of cheer in it. One sturdy iron hospital bed, one flimsy wooden chair occupied by a small boy called Michael, aged somewhere between four and six, high-ceilinged white-painted walls covered in scuff marks and a small bedside cabinet with a lukewarm jug of water and a used glass. In the bed was a man suffering from extreme head trauma, who at this point of waking didn't know his own name. It was James Knowles.

Most of the bricks from the chimney of the first house hit by the KLM DC-2 had landed either in the vicinity of James's head or directly on it. The first word he said after four months was 'Elsie'. The woman and the doctor entered the small hospital room. The child hadn't moved or spoken since his mother had left, but he thought the man in the bed looked like his father. His mum had told him that's who it was, but Michael thought he only looked a little bit like his father.

James had lost a lot of weight lying in the hospital bed for four months and, although tall, wasn't carrying any spare fat prior to the accident. Subsequently, the young boy, whose father spent days away from home working, had come to think of the man lying in the bed as a substitute father who never spoke and never came home at all now. It didn't matter to him, though, as he spent all his time with his mother. He preferred to call her Mum, but his mum asked him to call her Mother.

The doctor walked briskly over to his patient, who was looking from person to person trying to comprehend who, including himself, everyone was. The doctor did all the normal checks, shining a light into his patient's eyes, listening to his heartbeat through a stethoscope, taking his temperature and his blood pressure before looking down his throat and into his ears. James's hair was growing back over it, but he had a nasty five-inch scar on the back of his head plus several smaller lacerations that, all things considered, had healed quite nicely.

"Well, James, physically you have woken up in remarkably good health. We need to fatten you up somewhat but other than that, you're physically fine. We just need to give you some mental tests and observe you for a while, but your wife and son have every reason to expect you home in the medium future." The doctor looked at James like a dog who has sat up and begged for a biscuit and is awaiting its arrival.

James asked, "Wife and son?" He looked at Margaret Knowles, his lawfully wedded wife, and said, "You're not my wife. Are you Elsie?"

"Who's Elsie?" begged the openly weeping Margaret. The doctor took a step backwards.

"Who are you?" asked back James, neither wanting to answer each other's questions.

"I'm Margaret, your wife. And this," Margaret pulled her four-year-old son from the chair and pushed him to the side of the bed close to James's face, "this is your son, Michael. Do you not remember?" James closed his eyes; in fact, he scrunched his eyes up before opening them again. It was no good, he was still lying in a hospital bed not knowing his own name and certainly not knowing the woman and child stood in front of him claiming to be his wife and son.

The doctor, Worthington, it claimed on his badge, stepped towards Margaret.

"Mrs Knowles. It is far too soon to be confusing your husband. He's still in a state of shock and it could be a while, if ever, before he gets his full memory back."

"Ever!" Margaret, now sobbing, pulled Michael towards herself for comfort.

"Sorry, sorry, please don't get upset. This morning, your husband was in a coma and hadn't stirred since December last year and now he is here, talking to you. There is much to be grateful and hopeful for this morning. Only on rare occasions does a patient not get his or her memory back, but every solitary case involving heavy brain trauma, such as that experienced by your husband, is a different case. But let's be positive, today is a very big step forward in your husband's recovery."

James was trying to follow the conversation but there were too many words that he had to think too hard to understand the meaning of, so he gave up and let the noise of the doctor's voice wash over him. James asked, "I'm really sorry. I don't know my own name. Can someone please tell me?" He looked imploringly at the lady claiming to be his wife. A lady in a tightly belted, fastened spring coat in a complementary shade of green that matched her eyes and long auburn hair. She was beautiful, even if it was in an efficient way. Margaret turned those green eyes on her husband and made the doctor wish he had someone who looked at him like that.

"You are James Theodore Knowles. Husband of Margaret Knowles and father of Michael Knowles." Margaret pointed at herself and then her son. "We live not far from the hospital in Croydon, and you are a manager at Morris Motors. You travel the country selling cars for them and training others to sell cars." She then held her hand to her mouth. "I haven't even told them about your accident. I've been so shocked and coming here every day I didn't even think." None of this news meant anything to James. The only name he had in his head was 'Elsie'.

"I'm sorry for asking this but I have to ask as it's the only name that I seem capable of remembering. I assume it's a memory and not a figment of my imagination, but I need some clarity. Do you know who Elsie is?"

Margaret shook her head.

"There is no one we know called that name. Why do you keep asking?"

James, coming straight out of his coma, had no filter and before he could stop himself, he said the words, "Because my heart beats faster when I say the name, and the feeling behind the name is all love. When I say Elsie, I think it's someone I'm in love with." The hospital room went as cold as a crypt. James was very confused.

"Where am I again? Who are you? Who is the child?" Doctor Worthington started to earn his salary and suggested to Margaret and her son that they should leave now while the hospital continued to do tests on her husband. Michael thought he didn't want that man in the bed to be his dad if the man didn't know who he was. Life was simpler when you were four. Margaret left the hospital not knowing what to think. Getting her husband back was going to be more difficult than she thought.

Margaret came from money. Not the absolute upper classes of 'old' money, but she was brought up in a house not dissimilar to the one that Elsie was working in as James came out of his stupor. She drove a very nice new Morris Minor, secured at a very reasonable price by her estranged husband but thought it a 'little common' for her tastes. Her family had never thought the match an appropriate one, with James Knowles coming from the lower middle classes, but doted on their daughter to the extent that there was little she wanted that she didn't receive.

They didn't live in the style she had been raised in as James's income and her allowance from her father, which should have stopped when she married, did not stretch to a manor house. Nevertheless, they did live in a very select part of Croydon called Court Hill, a twenty-minute drive from the hospital that Margaret now knew as a second home after daily visits for over four months. Her parents were correct. The marriage had little chance of success, especially hindered by their lack of moral support. James had swept Margaret off her feet when they met in 1932 at the British International Motor Show held in Olympia, where James was representing the Morris Car company as an up-and-coming young salesman. There was nothing James couldn't sell and that included himself as Margaret, hampered somewhat by the presence of her parents, still managed to pick up one of the latest models. His name was James.

It was a whirlwind courtship. The wedding followed the engagement and then along came Michael. Margaret's family were at least enamoured by their first grandson, if not by their son-in-law. A whirlwind courtship is often followed by a whirlwind separation and divorce as the couple get to know each other and don't necessarily like what they find. She was spoilt, childish, uninterested in the world and its events, tied to her parents and incapable of making a decision as everyone had always made them for her.

He could be vulgar, unreliable, untidy, male chauvinistic, solitary, with little or no interest in Margaret's background and simply absent, both physically and mentally. They were two strikingly good-looking young people who had fallen in lust and not love and couldn't adapt to manage the consequences. James eventually left the family home, much to Margaret's chagrin. Not that she wanted him there but the shame of a failed marriage and having to listen to years of 'I told you so' from her parents meant she would rather they lived in the same house even if they didn't share the same bed.

That was not good enough for James. He couldn't live the lie. He found a cheap bedsit and travelled with work even more than he had before. When Margaret was contacted as next of kin, after the air crash, she deliberately didn't tell his employers, Morris Cars. She wanted him for herself.

The less he knew about his old life, the better, if she was to win him back. James lying in a coma in a hospital bed with her playing the grieving wife was almost a better outcome than having him leave her. What did she do now that he had risen from his bed? She knew straight away; she would mould him to the husband she thought she was getting the first time around. But who was Elsie?

James underwent test after test after test at Croydon Hospital, and April soon went, as did May, and his mind still would not kick-start again. His answers would vary from day to day, as would his test results. He now knew his name and that of his wife and child but had no recollection of his previous employment or his time travelling up to the north-west. He had a name, Elsie, but little else; the rest was just feelings. Strong, powerful feelings but nothing more. He believed he had a wife and son, he saw them most days, but his love for them was non-existent. He felt emptied out, as though someone had cut out that part of his brain in which they had previously lodged.

He was visited by his in-laws but knew nothing of them and took an instant dislike to their perceived superiority and sense of privilege. He stopped speaking to them completely and wouldn't utter a word until they left. His brothers made some small effort to come and see him, as did too his parents, but his knowledge of them was thin. He had been raised in a family that once you hit fourteen, you attained adulthood. It was you versus the world and you either won or lost. His memory allowed him to remember being a child, coupled with a deep river surrounded by trees with other boys playing around him, but it was as though he was sat in a movie theatre watching a film and once the film stopped, he could get up and leave.

What he did know, and it was already driving him to distraction, was that something was missing from within him. It sadly couldn't be filled by the woman called Margaret or the boy called Michael or any form of fraternal love. There was an emptiness to him, a void that couldn't be filled. A deep and soul-destroying itch that would never be scratched but one that he knew he would have to search to find a remedy for. He had a heartbreaking conversation with Margaret.

"They're going to let me out soon. They say they've done as much as they can for me, and they need the bed. Mum and Dad don't want me back at my age, and I can't come back to you. It's unfair on both of us. You are too young to waste your best years on me."

Margaret held her handkerchief to her eyes, but she was all cried out, apart from the crocodile ones she seemed able to produce at will. For James, this was the first time he had ever had this conversation, but Margaret was reliving events from over twelve months ago when James had left for the first time. They simply were not a couple. The couple was her and Michael, with James sat on the edge of the family looking in and occasionally making a guest appearance. They had slept in separate rooms for a while but with James being away with work so much, they had become increasingly estranged.

Even though James had been in a coma for several months, he came out of it with his subconscious still knowing that this relationship was over, and he now loved someone else. The problem he had was that no one south of Burnley knew of that relationship and all he had was a name, Elsie. He didn't have an address, not even a location or area; he couldn't even remember his previous occupation. Margaret handed over a piece of paper; she believed it was the least she could do.

"Here is the address of the bedsit where you were staying. It's in Purley. I don't know if they still have your things or not, but as you've left me and Michael once, there's nothing to come back for. I hoped we could try again, at least for Michael's sake, but you are right. I don't love you and you don't love me. It's sad but true. My father's solicitor will deal with the details of our divorce. Don't worry, if you don't want to see Michael, I don't need your money." Margaret leant across, kissed James on his stubbly cheek and left. The tears had dried up and her face was stern, like a headmistress about to address a class of unruly pupils. With a swish of her skirt, she was gone, forever.

Two days later, James was released from the hospital. He had an appointment to go back later that year, but it was one he would never keep. All he had in the world was the clothes on his body, a wallet with a few pound notes in it and a piece of paper with an address. His bedsit was on Hill Road, Purley. With some advice from the hospital reception, he was there within twenty minutes of brisk walking. He had been walking every day at the hospital since his recovery, but this still took it out of him. It wasn't just the walk; it was being outside again in the real world. He felt untethered; like he was a balloon held by a child and he was frightened that the child would let go and he would simply float away. By the time he arrived at his bedsit, he was puffing like an uphill train. He was greeted by a large, round landlady with a face like a bloodhound sniffing a trail.

"Mr Knowles. Didn't expect you back. Thought you'd done a runner. Your room has been taken. We've kept some of your things but sold most of your stuff to keep your room open for you. When it looked like you might never return, we just kept some personal stuff, just in case, you know."

James just nodded. His ex-landlady went rummaging out the back of the house and came back with a suitcase not dissimilar to the one Elsie had recently packed to take herself away to Blackburn.

"There you go, luvvie. Everything that's left. There's not much. A few clothes, papers, a wallet, not much to show for a man your age. Is there anything else I can do for you?"

James tried to regain some composure. He was lost, geographically and mentally.

"I have nowhere to stay," he said. "Do you have a room for the night just until I can get myself straight?"

"Well, it's not really a room. It's more like a shed. Well, to be honest, it is a shed, but we have a put-up bed you can sleep on in there for three bob tonight if you want? You'll have to come into the house for bathroom stuff, though. Plus, I'll throw in some toast and a cup of tea tomorrow morning for free."

"That would be great, thank you."

Those first twenty-four hours were the worst for James. Eventually, he contacted Morris Motors, his ex-landlady confirming where Margaret had said he previously worked, and after explanations they gave him a new job, not as well paid or as senior as his previous one, but he was earning again and earning enough to rent out a small one-bedroom flat. One thing he hadn't lost from his memory was the ability to sell, and the cars started to move off the showroom for him once more. He even managed a trip up to Burnley to the sales showroom there, but he never made it to Gawthorpe Manor as he had no recollection of ever being there. As he was still married, he had never told any of his Burnley colleagues about Elsie. Fred knew he had been seeing someone who rang the garage occasionally but was otherwise very unhelpful. Apparently, James was friendly with quite a number of the local girls.

The salesman who had spoken to Elsie decided she was better off without James. He avoided James and said little. Even when James told his story of the plane crash and coma, the tightly buttoned-up little man released no sympathy. The sooner 'Johnny-come-lately' buggered off back to London, the better, as far as he was concerned. If only James had been told that he had spent many an hour at the manor house, just a fifteen-minute walk from the High Street, he could have at least enquired there. The chances of Elsie being from there were very slim. James had stayed at more than ten different towns and cities up and down the country and he could have met Elsie in any one of them.

When back in London, James was coming to the conclusion that he would be living the rest of his life incomplete. He seemed to have a hole in his middle that no matter how much food or drink he consumed, or how many people he met and spoke to, could ever be filled. He lived with constant butterflies, examining every female face he saw in the hope that he may recognise someone.

In the north-west of England, Elsie had a baby boy and called him James, after his father.

James's life settled down into a routine of work, eat and sleep. He remembered little of 1938. He became anti-social outside of work but continued to retain the necessary charisma to do well in his chosen occupation. His life moved from day to day with no forward momentum other than the yearning in his chest that could never be sated. He worked, went back to his flat with the day's newspaper, read it cover to cover and after refuelling, because it couldn't be called dining, took himself off to bed to start the next day. Ironically, he slept better than he had in his entire life, as though he had nothing to dream about, or certainly no dreams that merited any remembering.

He never contacted any of his family and they never contacted him.

During 1938, Winston Churchill called upon America and Western Europe to prepare for armed resistance against

Hitler's Germany. In response, Adolf Hitler circulated amongst his high command a secret memorandum stating that they should prepare for the 'liquidation of the rest of Czechoslovakia'. This was closely followed by the extradition of all Jewish people with Polish citizenship from Germany. In Germany, the 'night of broken glass' began as Nazi activists and sympathisers looted and burned Jewish businesses. (The all-night affair saw 7,500 Jewish businesses destroyed, 267 synagogues burned, ninety-one Jewish people killed and at least 25,000 Jewish men arrested.)

In December 1938, Adolf Hitler was named *Times* magazine's 'Man of the Year'. Later that month, the Neuengamme concentration camp opened near Hamburg.

In 1939, the German military commenced preparations for the invasion of Poland. The only communication James had had with the outside world was the daily record of Hitler, Chamberlain, Mussolini and Edward Rydz-Śmigly (the commander-in-chief of the Polish armed forces), captured in the *Telegraph* newspaper. Some events were reported, some not, but James built his own picture of Adolf Hitler in his mind and found a goal for what remained of his life. He was always interested in politics and the warmongering of Europe's past before his accident, and somehow that part of his psyche had remained intact.

On the 1st of September 1939, Germany invaded Poland and World War II commenced. On the 2nd of September, James Knowles joined the war effort and eventually became a member of Montgomery's lads in the North African campaign.

His nickname in the war was 'Know-all Knowles', because he drove his tank into many battles with reckless abandon but always seemed to come out the other side. His reputation was fearless but there was a queue of soldiers wanting to be part of his crew because he always came through. Until he didn't.

Late March 1943, and the British Eighth Army bypassed the Axis defence on the Mareth Line after harsh fighting. The First Army in central Tunisia launched their main offensive in mid-April to squeeze the Axis forces until their resistance in Africa collapsed. During these skirmishes, the Crusader A-15 took a heavy artillery blow directly on top of the turret, almost breaking the tank into two pieces. James would carry a part of that tank with him for the rest of his life, as a piece lodged itself in his shoulder. He battled to fight himself clear, luckily with only light burns. His escape from the burning tank meant he never lost his tag as 'Know-all', but he never drove a tank again.

After release from army hospital, he held an administration role for the rest of the war before being demobbed late in 1946. The war was over; James had fought well for his country but came back to England aged forty-one with little to live for. He had experienced losses himself during the war; both his parents had passed away, both with cigarette-induced heart problems that neither of them even recognised until they were lying on the floor. Within four weeks of each other. By the time James found out, he was in the middle of a battle for Italian Libya.

He hadn't seen Margaret for many years. She had remarried an American man and James would never see her again as she was one of the 43,000 road fatalities in Great Britain between 1939 and 1944, peaking at over 9,000 in

1941. She was hit and killed instantly crossing the road in a London fog in 1943. Her father was seriously ill, and her mother was left as carer for her husband.

When James eventually found out, he took them to court for custody of his son, Michael, but the judge ruled he had been absent too long. James's attempt to become a father came too late, and he admitted to himself it was from a sense of duty rather than love. Michael remained with his ex-wife's parents until 1949 when at sixteen he put himself on a boat and sailed to America with his stepfather. He had a new name now and would not contact his blood father again.

During these years, James's brothers once more threw him a lifeline. They had decided in 1940, en masse, as a family to move to a country that they believed could offer them and their families better opportunities and a better quality of life than war-torn Europe could.

Since the early nineteenth century, Canada had been a popular destination for European immigrants. As far back as 1815 through to 1850, as many as 800,000 people left the United Kingdom to take up residence in the Canadian wilds. The period after World War II was known as the 4th wave of immigration in Canada, peaking at nearly 300,000 people in 1957. Immigrants from Britain were given highest priority. In terms of economic opportunity, Canada was most attractive to farmers headed for the Prairies, who typically came from eastern and central Europe. Immigrants from Britain preferred urban life. The Knowleses decided lock, stock and barrel to throw their lot in with the Canadians.

James simply could not leave. He was waiting for something, or someone, looking every day for a piece of his life that was missing. He had no affinity with his brothers and what fraternal love had briefly flared was extinguished by the crash of a plane and the trials of a terrible war. Standing proudly in his uniform, he said goodbye at Waterloo Station as what was remaining of his family headed off for Southampton docks and the ships to Canada. His brothers didn't really understand, but how could they, as James didn't understand himself.

After the war, and feeling cast adrift from life, he decided to try and reconnect with his youth. He went back to Hampton, where he had been dragged up by the reservoirs of south-west London. He walked the streets, reacquainting himself with Hampton Station, Bushy Park and, of course, the river Thames. It was amazing to him that he recognised all the places and reawakened memories lain dormant for over ten years. But still, he could not remember the few years prior to his memory loss. He even popped into the local public house, the Station, known locally and affectionately as the Dip due to a drop in the terrain as you approached the front of the pub.

Over several months he returned weekly to the London borough, trying to ignite his memories. He walked down the banks of the Thames to Hampton Court, remembering as a nine-year-old being dared to jump off the then bridge into the unpolluted clear waters below. A dare he won, until he arrived home for his normal punishment: a spell of solitary. It was a joyful upbringing with many happy memories that continually popped up in his mind like a slide show in his head. Could this be the link to his past that he needed to remember what was missing? To fill the hole that had been dug through his middle. James decided to move back, not only to Hampton, but he decided to try and buy his parents' old house, 39 Old Road.

He would reinvent himself. He wouldn't use his old name; he would change it. He knew of a family solicitor in the area, and he would work out what he could and couldn't legally do. In order to find the missing years of his life, he would hide the rest of it. No contact with his family abroad except through the solicitors. And he would find her, or she would find him. He could wait; he would wait. If this was the life promised to him then he would embrace it. But he would never give up hoping and praying that she would return, Elsie. He didn't even have an image of her in his head that he could recall in moments of sadness. All he had was an ache in his heart that over years would wane but never disappear.

The house came on the market and James was on hand to offer the full amount, no quibbling. He had funds, as apart from food and clothes, he never spent anything on himself. His small surpluses built into bigger amounts of money, and he had no problem in taking a small mortgage in 1953 and moving back to the house he was born in. The house cost James £2,000 and that was a bargain. A two-up two-down Victorian cottage with an outside toilet and a fair plot of land. His first thought was that the garden next door was beautiful, and he would have to up his game in the horticultural world if he wanted to live here again.

His life once again surprised him as he found himself living next door to the very same family of neighbours his parents had previously lived beside: the Churches. A large family whose children had all been a few years behind him and his brothers growing up. They therefore never mixed much but he knew his dad used to drink with old Mister Church in the Dip on the odd occasion when they bumped into each other. One of the grown-up lads had taken the house; Norbert, he thought his name was, known as Bert, and he had recently gotten himself married to a local girl who James didn't know.

James could start again but with all his childhood memories around him. No one knew him as the kid who had left home over twenty-five years ago. He was now an earlier-than- expected greying middle-aged man who looked older than his years, slightly thinner than comfortable and stooping below his natural height through years squashed into a tank. He would be fine back in Hampton, he thought, and took a job at the Hampton Water Treatment Works, so close to his home you could smell it, cycling to and from work every day. A simple life and one that enabled him to overcome his mental health issues with as little 'fuss' as possible.

As he aged, so did his friendship with Bert and Mary at number 41, and this also helped to stabilise him. It would be decades before he found the photos in a very old leather wallet of his sat at the top of the wardrobe in a battered tin cigar box, with the photographs tucked into the very bottom of the back section. The cigar box was in a decrepit cardboard suitcase that had sat on the top shelf of the wardrobe since he had returned to Hampton. The photos were creased and folded over and he hadn't even known they were there. He didn't remember the wallet or ever using it. When he found the photos, he wouldn't leave the house for several days. He didn't want anyone to see his tears.

St Helens, Lancashire

1937 Onwards

Elsie had run into the gloom like a B-movie heroine in one of the black and white films she watched at the cinema. Baby clutched to her chest, suitcase in her hand; she wondered if she would meet a hero who would save her and sweep her off her feet. Again. Not really expecting help from anyone, she went straight to the railway station and took the first train that came through. Somewhere was better than nowhere, she thought. The mist clung to her like a caul on a newborn baby as she boarded a train, last stop Preston, but if she changed at Preston junction, she could pick up a train to Southport. At least it was somewhere she vaguely knew as she had been there as a child on a day trip. Perhaps more than once, she thought, and it was only twenty miles from St Helens.

She knew she couldn't go home to her parents but her older sister Marie, already married, wouldn't turn her away. But her sister was to be her last resort. She was going to see what Southport brought to her first.

She had money to set herself up in a boarding house; one thing about a seaside resort outside the season, there was plenty of cheap accommodation. No one knew her in Southport; she could use her own name without fear of reprisal and use the cover story that she was a widow, not a single mum. Finding a cleaning role, she earned nine shillings a week and paying the landlady's daughter sixpence a day to look after James, plus her room and breakfast, she got by. She just about had enough money left to buy the baby food and the occasional clothes.

Once in a while, she was obliged to dip into her savings, her savings being the pawn money received for her never-to-be-used engagement ring. James was one year old when the pawn money remaining added to less than the price of a bottle of milk. Elsie's earnings had now become less than the cost of living plus providing for the baby. She ate less and less herself until she became ill in October 1938. So ill she couldn't work. She packed her suitcase, held together with string and determination, and with just enough money remaining to get a train to St Helens she left the seaside resort.

Even though the two places are only seventeen miles apart, Elsie had to take a train from Lord Street in Southport to Liverpool Lime Street and then change there to St Helens Central Station, renamed in 1949 as Shaw Street Station. The whole journey took her well over two hours and she was left with a one-and-a-half-mile walk carrying a crying James every step of the way. She turned up on her sister's doorstep in Harris Avenue wet from the drizzle, still ill from a sustained time of not enough food, with a baby that had had its last milk six hours earlier and not a penny in her purse.

As any sister would have done under similar circumstances, Marie welcomed Elsie back into the family. The question still remained how the rest of the family would react to the baby, with no gold band on Elsie's finger.

Marie had married David Holmes several years ago and they already had three boisterous and healthy children, two now young adults, to care and worry about. The eldest, Frank, was aged nineteen, then came May, aged seventeen, and little Kenneth, aged five. Between May and Ken, there had been numerous pregnancy problems and birth issues which had kept the children to three.

While Marie showed her sister and nephew all the compassion she could muster, she still had a houseful of her own family to care for as well. Her husband, David, was also understanding rather than compassionate, but helped accommodate his sister-in-law by building an extra bunk bed with his own hands from spare bits of wood from the factory floor where he worked. In an already full household, two more warm bodies were introduced. When Elsie left the house, she ensured she walked out with her sister, who pushed the pram accordingly should they bump into anyone. While there was undoubted talk around the streets, the lines became blurred between Frank, May, Ken and now James, and equally so between Marie and Elsie.

There were still the parents to face. Mrs Scott would have taken Elsie and James back into her household, but Mr Scott simply could not face the shame or the disgrace. As long as 'our Marie' would look after them, he pretended he didn't care. It seemed that his stubbornness would become a family trait. Elsie and Marie would meet their mother in the park or go for a walk and that way Mrs Scott at least met her grandchild, but Elsie, as was the way, was ostracised.

James was two years and three months old, almost Christmas 1939, when events came to a head. Elsie had been applying for jobs in service once again and with more and more lads joining the forces, women in work were becoming a far regular sight. She registered herself with an agency that provided service staff to stately homes and through sleight of hand with her name and marital status bagged herself a role at a stately home, Bolton Hall in Wensley, Yorkshire. One of her selling points was a little experience coupled with the facility to 'travel anywhere'. Marie and David would have liked to have been included in the application process.

"You said what?" asked Marie. "How can you travel anywhere with a child?"

"Well, they don't know about James."

"Not many people do," added David, from behind his copy of the *Reporter*, not even bothering to lower his paper to join the conversation.

"If I had put that I have a kid, I'd never have gotten a job. I need a job so I can help you out with money. I can't stay here all me life."

"No, you can't," said David.

Marie looked genuinely at a loss to express her disgust to her sister.

"Let me get this right. You want me to look after James while you go and get a job, live the life of Riley, and send us a bob or two when you have it." At that moment, Frank, eldest son, walked into the room.

"All right, Mum, Dad, Aunty Elsie. What's all the shouting about?"

"Frank, go and get changed out of your work clothes. Me and your aunty are having a private discussion. Go upstairs now." Frank never thought twice about disobeying his mum. He might be nineteen but 'Respect your parents' was a mantra this family lived by.

"Marie, I won't be living any life. I've made a stupid mistake, a big one, I know, but if you'd ever worked in service, you'd know I won't be living any high life. The only chance of paying you back any small amount for what you've done for me is if I get a job. To get a job, I have to move away. If I move away and take James, I can't work. So, I stay here under your feet and contribute nothing." Annoyingly for Marie, she could see the logic of Elsie's argument.

"You want to leave James here with me then? But for how long?"

"I honestly don't know. A couple of years. I'll be back twice a year when I get some time off. This is a real chance. Bolton Stately Home is a proper big mansion house, and they pay better than most, which, apart from some pin money, I promise I'll send straight to you for help in raising James."

Marie pondered her next statement, but sisters rarely hold back with one another.

"You'll never see him. He won't know you. You'll just keep moving on from job to job. After everything you went through to get him out of that home in Blackburn."

"I will see him. Just not as much as I would like to but it's that or at some time in the future, me and James will end up in the poor house." Elsie was playing the 'sympathy card' early, but Marie hadn't been raised a fool either.

"You know damn well that'll never happen. Even Dad wouldn't let that happen."

David Holmes looked at them both from behind his paper.

"If you two are going to start cursing, you can go and argue in the yard. We won't have language like that from either of you." And then back to the racing pages.

Elsie continued.

"I really haven't had much luck. Once, and I got caught, and then the bloke runs out on me. If I don't have this job, then I will have nothing. My life will be over before it's ever got started."

Marie pauses, wanting to gather her thoughts. She thinks she's now arguing for the sake of it, just to beat her younger sister rather than for anyone's benefit. She says, "Wait here. I'm going to peg this washing out. Then I'll be back."

Three weeks and numerous arguments that then became discussions later, Marie sticks her head in the door. Elsie is trying to look busy by the sink.

"David, come in the yard, please," she requests. With a play show of annoyance, David folds his paper up, sticks it down the side of the old armchair that looks older than the house, and heaves himself from the barely held together ball of stuffing. Under his breath, he mouths, "Takes a man…"

Outside, there is furtive whispering and even a couple of chuckles from David before they come in again. Marie fills her lungs as though she's about to sing and, on the exhale, says, "Okay, we will do it, but there are certain rules and restrictions that we have to insist on." Not knowing what's about to be said, Elsie merely shrugs. Marie continues.

"James becomes ours. Me and David's. We adopt him. James and little Kenny have been getting on like brothers and although Ken can be a bit rough with him, he loves him. It's almost easier for us to have the two of them rather than Kenny on his own. Now that Frank and May are so grown up, they don't have as much time for Ken as they once did. We didn't mean to leave such a big gap; God just judged us that way. So, we will adopt James and we'll raise him as our fourth child."

The room became silent.

"And will I be able to see him?" asked Elsie.

"Whenever you come home, whether for good or between jobs, there will always be a bed here for you. You can see him but as Aunty Elsie. James can call me Mum and David's his dad from now on in. I honestly think it'll be the best for James. Imagine the stick he'd get at school if he 'didn't have a mum or dad'. He can go to St Theresa's, where Ken will be going, and they'll just be known as brothers. Kenneth and James Holmes. Not James Scott. It works, Elsie, and you know I'd look after him as though he were my own."

"But what would people think?" asked Elsie.

"There are no people to think," answered the older sister. "You've hardly gone out since you came back. People have assumed he's mine anyway. There's been that many comings and goings over the years. Half the neighbours are new. Anyone who saw us out walking just thought he was mine, as I did the pushing. Mum and Dad know but they won't say anything. We can swear Frank and May to silence. They won't go against us. By the time James Scott goes to school, he will be James Holmes and then it's on the school register. We can get the papers done before you take this job."

"And what about James, will he ever know?" asked Elsie. Frank has been stood in the hallway listening to the debate from start to finish. *If it's anything to do with me he'll be told one day, when he needs to know*, he thinks.

Marie answers. It seems she has thought of everything.

"I will never tell him. If I raise him as my son, he will be my son. My answer to you would be once you've decided this is the path you wish to take, could you put him through the torment of finding out that you abandoned him when he was aged two?"

Abandon. That was a word that hadn't entered Elsie's head until that moment.

"But I don't want to abandon him, as you put it. I have nowhere to go and no way of supporting myself. I just want you as my sister to mind him for a while."

"Elsie, I have told you what we have to do, and I think it would be for the best for you and for James if he became Ken's little brother. No one would ever need to know. If at some time in the future, you think the time is right to let him know then that's your call. One more thing, when we adopt and change his name, I want to change his name to Holmes as you know but also, I want to add John as a middle name. It was David's grandad's name, and it will mean he's a real Holmes."

"So, his new name will be James Harold John Holmes?"

"If you agree to us adopting him." The sisters went on discussing this long into the night with neither side's argument changing that much. It was the age-old contradiction of nurture versus nature. Elsie slept little and the night frights gripped her like a hot cocoon, drenching the small put-up bed she slept in. She eventually concluded that James would be better off with her sister's family and that in a couple of years' time she would come back and reclaim him.

A week later and the paperwork had been completed. James was a Holmes and would remain so until the day he died in 2016.

Elsie was sat alone on a train chugging its way through the Pennines, dwarfed by the hills and valleys of the majestic Yorkshire Moors. In her mind's eye, she had the next ten years all mapped out.

She didn't want to give James up for adoption. She had fought like a hellcat to release him from the prison in Blackburn. (To herself, she made it seem like she had escaped from a high-security prison by fighting off several guards, not walking from a home managed by Catholic nuns.) Interestingly, her parents had agreed that Marie taking James was the best outcome for everyone, and her father had even taken to saying morning and afternoon to her. A start, she supposed. Elsie was stubborn as well and, apart from one small indiscretion under the stairs at Gawthorpe Manor, didn't believe she had done too much wrong. It's amazing how resilient our minds can be when assimilating half-truths to suit a particular narrative. Just ask any politician.

In her future history, she was going to return, after a number of years in service, with enough saved funds to rent or buy a little place off Cook Street, near to where Marie lived. Her new fiancé would come with her, and they would be wed. She would claim James back and after some tears and hand wringing, Marie would see it was for the best. Then she would have a couple more children and James would be the eldest of three. The stigma would be lifted. Elsie thought that being a Catholic, it should be stigmata, not stigma, as they wanted to brand you for life.

That was her future history, one that would not follow that exact journey on the playbill of her life. In what would become a life penance, she would never know her first child as a mother knows her son. Her thoughts also turned to James Theodore Knowles. What had ever become of him? What would become of him? She truly thought he loved her, and she knew she had loved him. She would always carry him with her wherever she went. She had no closure. No final argument, no shouting and screaming insults at each other, no quiet discussion that things hadn't worked out and they should go their separate ways.

Elsie just didn't know how but in order to move on, she had to believe that, in the end, James the father had not wanted her, and he didn't even know about James the son. Now to be raised by his aunty and uncle. Squashed between two oversized farmworkers, she looked out of the train window and absorbed the raw beauty of the Yorkshire countryside. She would make a life for herself; she was too stubborn to do anything else, and she would pass that stubbornness on to her son. He would have the same genes as Elsie and later in life would not move from his perceived truth. They would both become victims of their own DNA.

Elsie would never stop checking the face of every man

she would ever see or meet. Is that him, who's that tall man by the bar, the set of a pair of shoulders, the smart pinstripe suit? She would spend her life wishing, looking and searching for the man she would always truly love.

St Helens, Merseyside

1975

Summer had come and gone, and Graham was back at school trying to hold on to the biggest secret of his life so far. A secret that was a proper grown-up secret, not just who had been smoking at the back of the bike sheds at school. His dad's family was not really his family. He was in his room with his best mate, Charlie, and Anne and David kept popping in and out making noise.

It was Sunday, 21st September, and they were trying to tape some of the Sunday night charts off the radio. From five until 7pm every Sunday, Tom Browne presented the new Top Forty pop singles in the UK. Graham and Charlie tried to get their particular favourites taped on Anne's cassette player by pressing play and record at the same time as having the radio next to the cassette recorder.

This week, they wanted *That's the Way (I like It)*, by KC & the Sunshine Band; *Funky Moped*, by Jasper Carrott; *There Goes My First Love*, by the Drifters (but they couldn't tell anyone at school about that one) and *Hold Me Close* by David Essex, and Graham's mum had asked him to tape Rod Stewart singing *Sailing*, who had been number one for about three years. Charlie had to go straight home after the chart show finished, Sunday night and all that, and Graham made his way to the living room to get the best seat for Sunday night viewing. When there were five seats and five people, it paid to be prompt.

There was a new Australian series on BBC1 about a bush ranger called Ben Hall that he knew his mum would hate but he hoped to watch the start of before *Upstairs Downstairs* came on ITV later. He also hoped to pull his dad to one side as he had been storing some questions up about his dad's true mother that he wanted answering.

Anne and David were upstairs getting ready for bed, and Graham waited for his dad to go into the kitchen and make a cup of tea before surreptitiously following him. A dangerous move, he knew, as if one of those two muppets came downstairs, they would 'nick' his seat. But he needed a private chat.

"Dad," he exclaimed before his dad had even seen he was in the room, causing him to spill the milk.

"Bloody hell, son. The devil makes more noise than you. What do you want? David will have your seat if you're not quick."

"I've been thinking about that story you told me. You know when I found 'that stuff' under the stairs. Can I ask you a couple of questions?"

James Holmes took a deep breath and exhaled through his nose. Not quite sighing but making a good impression of a bull in a field.

"Go and set the chess set up in the back room. We'll have a game away from the telly. We might get a bit of quiet, let's see."

Graham did as he was asked while his dad took the tea into the front room to Lizzie, who was settling down with John Alderton and Gordon Jackson in the Downstairs part of Eaton Place, Belgravia. He returned with his own 'brew' and sat opposite Graham at the dining-room table, which doubled up as a games table on chess nights. (It was also a table tennis table when required.)

"So, what's bothering you?" he asked his son.

Looking at the chess pieces intensely, even though the first move was yet to be made, Graham said, "I just want to know a bit more about your real mum. My real grandma. I know she handed you over to her sister, but why, and what happened next?"

"I can try and answer, but I don't know everything myself. She handed me over because she didn't want me. She abandoned me."

That word again, thought Graham.

"I don't know all the ins and outs, but she had a job in Yorkshire and couldn't take me. Her sister Marie, who I called Mum for the rest of her life, said that she would only take me if it was for real. Proper, with full adoption. So, my real mum said yes. Think about how I felt finding out in that letter from Frank."

"But, Dad, she's your real mum."

"If she was my real mum, she wouldn't have given me away. Anyway, that's all over now because she's dead, at least she's dead to me. But you asked what happened next." It hadn't passed Graham by that his dad had said 'dead to me' and not just dead. "As far as I know, she had a few jobs all over the place and met a new bloke who didn't know about me and so married her. Then they had a couple of kids of their own. When my mum and dad, Marie and David Holmes, passed away, she was at the funerals but never spoke to me other than as an aunty who I didn't know that well.

"Your Aunty May then raised us – me and Ken – in Harris Avenue until we were adults. I thought May was my sister until the letter told me she was my cousin. During this time, my real mum could have sought me out and told me, but she didn't. She had her own little family, and I wasn't part of it. I guess she thought what I didn't know couldn't hurt me. Well, I did find out and it's hurt me every single day since."

"So, who knows or knew then?" asked the bewildered Graham

"Frank and May knew. I guess some of my other uncles and aunties who we never see anyway. Ken now knows but I think he found out when I did. Me, your mum, your Nana and Grandad Prescott and, of course, Elsie Scott, now Elsie Tremain. As you like to call her, 'my real mum'. And now you, son. There may be others who know but no one says owt about it. It was such a long time ago now."

"And there is no way in your heart that you want to see her and find out from her what really happened?" Graham felt that there had been a role reversal here and he was the father, and his dad was the son.

His dad said, "I know what happened. She didn't want me, and no lies today, years later, will change that." Neither of them actually knew what it was like to be a single mother in the late 1930s. Neither of them fully understood that the stigma, even then in 1970s England, was still a burden to carry and, if carried, almost impossible to live with. James was stubborn, a trait his mother had difficulty managing within herself all those years ago and a trait that also made him a victim of his own DNA. Their similarity was the barrier that kept them apart.

Graham and his dad had their game of chess. Graham won easily. His dad wasn't able to concentrate on the battle in front of him when every day of his life he had to concentrate on the battle raging in his own head. After a while, Graham stopped asking his dad about his past and, as most teenagers will do, concentrated on the present.

Many months later, he was walking through the town centre market with his dad and siblings and an older lady stopped to speak to his dad. His dad didn't see her and continued his shuffle through the packed market stalls, keeping his eyes on his three kids, weaving in and out of the crowds. Years later, Graham would find out that his real grandmother had tried to approach them, but his father, James, had walked on. It was so many years later when he was told that Graham's grandmother had already died. Graham, Anne and David would be eighteen, sixteen and fourteen respectively when she passed away. They never met her.

Highcliffe, Dorset

Christmas, 2019

Every year was different. When you had four children, two siblings, several sets of in-laws and a couple of widows, not to mention several divorces, Christmas was different every year. Especially when your two sons lived in Japan and America. Christmas Day itself was going to be a quiet one for Graham and Jayne, with just Jayne's mum, Mary, putting in her attendance on the day. The weekend before – Saturday the 21st and Sunday the 22nd – would be full, though, with Julie, Graham's eldest and the two granddaughters; Susan and her boyfriend, Fergal; Graham's sister, Anne, and her partner, Colin, and of course Mary as well.

The house was just about big enough if Julie shared a room with the girls and they put Mary in a taxi as she only lived a couple of miles away. Jayne had decided that as she would be cooking for the next two weeks, or near as damn it, they could eat takeaway, and the family room dining table was filled with Chinese from the Far East, the local oriental restaurant.

The table was full. Appetisers first: prawn crackers (anything over £50, they were free, and Graham knew this lot was going to be eye-watering to his credit card), chicken satay, sesame prawn toast, grilled pork dumplings, two lots of spring rolls – meat and veggie – plus crispy aromatic duck with pancakes. And that was just the starters. Mains followed: beef in black bean sauce, salt and peppered chicken, ginger and spring onion lamb, twice-cooked beef, sweet and sour chicken balls, king prawn Kung Po and several chow mein and numerous special fried rice.

"I hope you're all hungry," said Graham. "Let battle commence." And it did. Jayne was forever amazed at the tenaciousness of Graham's family when it came to food. As an only child in Old Road, she had never had to get her elbows out and mark her territory or make a strong claim on the last piece of bread. She and Graham had done their utmost when bringing up his four kids at weekends to present them with table manners, but get them all together and, to quote Graham, 'It's hey boys hey', whatever that northern expression actually meant. There was more than enough for all. Plus seconds and even thirds, as well as a Chinese breakfast the next morning straight from the fridge.

After dinner, the room split up, with many going into the television room to watch either a film or sport. Liverpool were playing Flamengo of Rio, Brazil in the World Club Final, but there was going to be a fight for the telly as the Bond film *Casino Royale* was on the other side.

"It's the one with Craig, not David Niven," said Graham.

"Is he showing off his film knowledge again?" asked Anne. She knew her older brother only too well. "Don't you worry about the telly anyway," she continued, "I want to tell you about my trip to Canada." Anne, Jayne, Susan and Graham stayed in the family room as everyone else went to fight over channels in the movie room. It was just a normal room with a big screen and surround sound, but Graham 'fancied himself' somewhat and so called it a 'movie room'. 'Fancied himself' as per his siblings anyway. Jayne was also amazed that the three northern siblings (David was absent) didn't let each other get away with anything. If there was a chance of a laugh at each other's expense, they took it, and it didn't matter who it was in front of. They were unforgiving.

Graham poured them all a nice drop of shiraz and Susan took the floor, her long bird- like limbs tucked around her as though she were nesting.

"This is as far as I've got. I've written out the bits you'll be interested in rather than trying to use the website. Here's a copy."

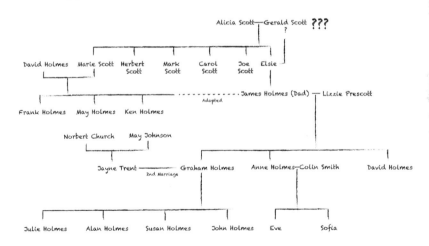

Anne proceeded to hand out a handwritten copy of a family tree, their family tree. Jayne's mum, Mary, came back in from the movie room as this was more interesting than either Bond or Liverpool.

"Okay, listen up. It shouldn't be too difficult as we know most of this. I'll start at the top. Alicia Scott and Gerald Scott had six kids at the earliest part of the twentieth century and late nineteenth century for the oldest. Marie was the oldest and married David Holmes, who had Frank, May and Ken. Graham, you'll know better than me, but to us that was Uncle Frank, Aunty May and Uncle Ken. Then Elsie had a baby out of wedlock, Dad, and for whatever reason gave him to Marie to raise. Dad met Mum, got married, went off to Hong Kong and came back a different person, literally. Then us three were born and I've not put all the weddings and divorces on here, but you all know who you are and where you fit into this tree.

"But we still have a huge question mark? WHO WAS DAD'S BIRTH FATHER? I've still not been able to find out, but I have got a few clues from my trip to Canada." Anne paused and took a large gulp of shiraz.

"As you all know, we got a hit on the DNA sample I gave from the website company, Hereditary. So, I went off to Canada to meet this lady who had similar DNA to me. And, therefore, to you as well, Graham."

"Thanks for that, Anne. I'd be lost without you."

"He's been sarcastic since he was six and never lost the knack," answered Anne.

Susan chipped in. "At least I know where we all get it from, Dad."

"Leave me alone, it's nearly Christmas," he play sulked. "Carry on, Anne, have you found anything?"

"There is a high probability that me and this girl, Melanie Belanger, that's her name, could be cousins. Her family left England during World War Two and moved to Canada. Better prospects and all that. She had four great-uncles who were the mainstay of the family and once they decided to go, the whole family went." Graham butted in.

"But what's that got to do with us?"

"Well, the DNA check says there is a high probability that one of those brothers, or a close relative of them, could be related to us and it could be, not certainty, but could be our paternal grandfather. Dad's dad!"

Each person was impacted in a slightly different manner to the news that Anne shared. To start, Anne herself was proud of the fact that she had decided to investigate in the first place. One, she'd had to wait for her dad to pass away before she could start the process and secondly because she'd been able to smash her own personal shell she was trapped in and go on an adventure to Canada to meet a stranger. Graham was pleased for Anne and truly excited that they at long last may know who their grandfather had truly been.

Susan's excitement was as a direct consequence of her dad's excitement, plus potentially finding out where she originally came from was a pretty cool thing to do. Jayne and her mother, Mary, were a little further removed from the epicentre of this prospective emotional earthquake. Jayne could see the twinkle in her husband's eye and the passion flowing from him and his sister. Mary, who was approaching ninety years of age, drew on the past. She could remember the times that these relatives of her son-in-law had lived, and she thought about the losses she had experienced in her own life, including the loss of her dear husband, Bert. A lonely shiraz-fuelled tear weaved its way down her lined face.

The space around the table twinkled with the candles scattered around the room, and the Christmas lights accompanied them from the small tree at the far end of it. Ornaments adorned every window sill and shelf, and the large south-facing windows bared a stark night sky with a watery winking half-moon casting an eerie light over the garden. The room had momentarily gone quiet before everyone started talking again, and several conversations took place at once.

Finally, Anne pulled out an orange document box of the type that still filled room after room in solicitors' and accountants' offices. She said, "I have more stuff to show you that I picked up from Mel in Canada. I just told you about four brothers, the Knowleses, who moved across to Canada, but one of the brothers didn't go. Apparently, he had a mental breakdown after coming back from the war and decided not to go to Canada but stayed in London. Actually, I don't know that, but he didn't go to Toronto, and he deliberately only contacted his brothers through his solicitor so that no one knew where he was."

Graham asked, "Why would anyone do that? Doesn't make sense."

"As I said, he had mental health issues because of the war, plus, on top of that, he had an accident just before the war. I don't know the details, but he couldn't remember who he was for a while and didn't get his full memory back. Anyway, he didn't want anything to do with his family and said he was looking and waiting for someone. He was married with a son but that all went west, and she died young, and his son went off to America, never to be heard from again."

Graham again chipped in. "Bloody hell, he didn't have much luck, this bloke, did he? What else do we know about him?"

"That's about it really. Mel thinks he changed his name because he literally disappears from all records, but then when he died, this box of personal items got sent by his solicitor to one of his brothers and it eventually got passed down to Mel. These are just copies. Mel kept the originals."

Anne opened the box and passed the photocopies of documents around the table. There was a will, a birth certificate and a marriage certificate. Copies of bank transfers from the sale of a property but with the address redacted. All very old and hardly legible, especially in a photocopy. Nevertheless, the documents were fascinating. It was as though a slice of history had been released into the room, where it drifted around the inhabitants like a sea mist on a beach.

The chatter was like the monkey house at the zoo as everyone was trying to show everyone else something they had read or couldn't read. Papers were passed around and held up to the light for a better view. Graham got up and put the main light on, destroying the mood but enabling people's ability to see what they were looking at.

Then Jayne went ashen. She stopped what she was doing, and her face went as pale as the half-moon in the winter's sky. She stood up quickly and her chair scraped along the floor behind her, causing everyone to stop what they were doing. Then, she upped and left the family room and Graham heard the internal door to the garage crash open.

Everyone looked at each other and Graham simply said, "Mad as a hatter. I'll see what she's doing. If she wanted more wine, she only had to ask."

He followed his wife into the garage, where he found her moving large plastic see- through boxes around. They had been in the new house two years now, but the garage was still full of things that were either going to stay there forever or, when a decision was made sometime in the next seven years, get taken to the dump.

"Graham, where's all my old stuff from the loft in Old Road?"

"I believe it's in one of these boxes, love. But I think you know that."

Jayne was now tearing the lids off the boxes and, most unlike her, not replacing them as she went to the next one and ripped that off also.

"What are you looking for, Jayne?" Graham now looked quite exasperated.

"The stuff that was in the loft in Hampton. I've told you."

"That's right at the back as we never even opened them. Wait a minute." Graham then waded through the open boxes to those at the rear and took a more measured approach. He had never seen Jayne like this in his entire life, she was literally frantic, and Graham didn't like it. When someone acts completely out of character, it can spook people who are close to them, and that's how Graham felt looking at his wife.

After a couple of minutes' searching, he found the right box. Jayne pulled the lid off and after lifting a couple of strange items, old baby clothes, a knitted shawl, some small children's vanity cases, she picked up a faded coloured box and said to Graham, "Got it. Come on, love, back to the others. You're not going to believe this."

Running to the kitchen, her new Christmas outfit covered in dust and cobwebs, Jayne pushed everything on the table out of the way. She placed in the centre the photocopy that Anne had brought back from Canada with her.

Jayne asked Anne, "Tell me again where this photo came from?"

Anne wasn't sure where Jayne was going with this but answered. "It was sent to Canada when the brother who stayed home died. James Theodore Knowles, he was called. We don't know who she is, although she does have a look of Mel. There were few photos taken back in the 1930s of ordinary people so we figured it might have been a film star or something. Mum does think it looks like Marie, Dad's stepmum, who adopted him, but I think she's seeing what she wants to see."

Jayne then opened the box that she had been given all those years ago when it had been stuffed with money and a letter as well as a photograph. She pulled the old photo out with no ceremony, this was not a time for magic tricks, and laid it next to the photocopy from Canada.

Susan was the first to speak.

"It's the lady I saw in the bathroom mirror all those years ago. She wants to be found." And then, with no explanation, she burst into tears.

Anne and Graham were stunned into silence until Anne asked the question that they all wanted to know the answer to: "Who is it, Jayne, and where did you get it from?"

Jayne looked around at each person in the room, lingering slightly longer on her husband before responding.

"I don't know who she is, but Uncle Ted gave her to me."

39 Old Road, Hampton

1914

Epilogue

On 1st January 1914, the first commercial flight carrying paying passengers takes off in America, specifically Florida to Tampa. On 28th June, Archduke Franz Ferdinand of Austria is assassinated by Serbian nationalist Gavrilo Princip, heralding the start of the Great War. On 5th August in Ohio, America, the first electric traffic light is installed in Cleveland. On Thursday, 27th August, on Hampton Court Bridge, Middlesex, England, James Theodore Knowles, aged nine, jumps off the top of the bridge into the clear Thames below because one of his brothers 'dares' him to do so.

"You are in big trouble now, James," said George, one of the four brothers. "Mother is going to kill you. She specifically said don't get those new shorts ruined and now they're wet through."

James clutched a red bouncy ball in his hand. His pride and joy. He went everywhere with it in his pocket. It was only a penny rubber ball but for some reason James had been drawn to it like a tramp to a free meal. Water pooled around his feet.

"If you hadn't thrown my ball in and then dared me to go and get it, I wouldn't be wet through," he wailed back. Life was so unfair as he knew his mother would indeed hold him responsible for his own actions. One thing about the Knowles family was that you never relinquished your own responsibility or accountability. George did feel a little sorry for his younger brother but not too much.

"Come on, by the time we get home, you'll be dry." The walk home was about a mile and a half along the dusty, dirty river road which in 1914 was only partly paved. James arrived at his front door, 39 Old Road, Hampton, covered in so much grey dust that he looked like he'd done a shift at the cement works.

Mother didn't shout; she screamed.

"Do you ever, ever, ever listen to what I say to you, James Knowles? You know where you're going for the rest of the day, now get." James hung his head like a man walking to the gallows as he dragged his feet to the coal hole under the stairs. Opening the latch, he went in and sat on the bottle crate that had been specifically placed for his misdemeanours. Unfortunately for James, living in a two-up two-down Victorian cottage meant he shared a bedroom with three other brothers. *Thank the lord they are all boys*, thought Mother. So, when he misbehaved, which was at least once a week, instead of being shown to his room, he was thrown under the stairs. It became his second home, as someone else was always using the bedroom for something.

He sat on the crate, pulled his ball from his damp but drying pocket and threw it against the internal wall the house shared with number 41. Floor first, then wall, then back into his waiting hand. Sometimes, to break the monotony, he would go wall first, then floor, then back to his hand, but somehow that was more difficult and he ended up scrabbling in the coal, looking for his red ball. If he left his punishment cell dirtier than he went in, he'd go without supper. He threw the ball. Rhythmic, consistent; badaam, badaam, badaam. Throw, double bounce, catch. Throw, double bounce, catch.

The bouncing ball echoed, not only through the house but through time itself, and in 41 Old Road, in the year 2007, James Knowles's great-granddaughter heard the bouncing ball and was terrified. Whether she heard the retained energy in the house from the young boy's angst as he was trapped under the stairs or James's spirit after he had passed away in 1978, she would never know. Was James reaching out to his great-granddaughter, trying to tell her what she didn't know? *Susan, I am here.*

James eventually fell asleep, head resting against the wall, chilled by the wet and the damp under the stairs. He dreamt and in his dream he saw a woman; it was his mother. She was stood in front of a big house, like Hampton Court Palace. Every little boy's first love is their mother and James was no exception. In his dream, he felt that overwhelming love for her, that unconditional love that starts in the breast and evolves into something magnificent and terrifying. He woke in a cold sweat but remembering his daydream.

The door to the coal hole opened and his mother stood there with the light shining bright behind her. James thought she looked like an angel and threw his arms around her, tears welling up in his eyes. She removed his arms, uncomfortable with the unexpected show of affection, and then James said the strangest thing to her, which she later dismissed as him falling asleep and dreaming: "Don't worry, Mother, I'll wait for her. I'll wait as long as it takes. Even if it takes forever."

In 2007, Susan heard a ball bouncing and saw a lady in the mirror.

Alan J Hill lives in Christchurch, Dorset, and is a semi-retired finance professional after working in the industry for over forty years. He most recently worked for Autism Wessex as a Finance Director and continues to dedicate himself to the non-profit sector. Alan has been involved in community sport all his life and has won awards for his coaching. He is the author of *A Boy Called Arsenal*, the eye-opening biography of Arsenal Whittick, and the children's book *The Yarns of Sid Seven-Legs*.

For writing and publishing news, or
recommendations of new titles to read,
sign up to the Book Guild newsletter: